# Information Technology

## *Made Simple*

The Made Simple series
has been created
especially for self-education
but can equally well
be used as
an aid to group study.
However complex the subject,
the reader is taken
step by step,
clearly and methodically,
through the course. Each volume
has been prepared by experts,
taking account of
modern educational requirements,
to ensure the most
effective way of
acquiring knowledge.

# In the same series

Accounting
Advertising
Auditing
Biology
Book-keeping
British Constitution
Business Calculations
Business and Enterprise Studies
Business and Commercial Law
Calculus
Chemistry
Child Development
Commerce
Computer Electronics
Computer Programming
Computer Typing
Cost and Management Accounting
Economic and Social Geography
Economics
Education
Electricity
Electronics
Elements of Banking
English
Financial Management
First Aid
French
German
Graphic Communication
Information Technology

Italian
Latin
Law
Management Theory and Practice
Marketing
Mathematics
Modern European History
Modern World History
MSX
Music
Office Practice
Personnel Management
Philosophy
Photography
Physical Geography
Physics
Politics
Psychiatry
Psychology
Russian
Salesmanship
Secretarial Practice
Social Services
Sociology
Spanish
Statistics
Statistics for Business
Teeline Shorthand
Typing

# Information Technology

## *Made Simple*

Roger Carter

**MADE SIMPLE**
**B O O K S**

Made Simple
An imprint of Butterworth-Heinemann Ltd
Linacre House, Jordan Hill, Oxford OX2 8DP

PART OF REED INTERNATIONAL BOOKS

OXFORD   LONDON   BOSTON
MUNICH   NEW DELHI   SINGAPORE   SYDNEY
TOKYO   TORONTO   WELLINGTON

First published 1991

© Roger Carter 1991

**British Library Cataloguing in Publication Data**
Carter, Roger
  Information technology made simple.
  – (Made simple)
  I. Title   II. Series
  004

ISBN 0 7506 0141 8

Printed and bound in Great Britain by
Biddles Ltd, Guildford and King's Lynn

# Contents

# Preface

Information technology (IT) today handles information in every conceivable form, whether music, video, graphics, speech, data, text. It also embraces an increasing range of technologies. Smart cards, computer animation, interactive compact discs, computer-based training, computer-integrated manufacturing, virtual reality systems, the list is endless. This book surveys the full range of IT topics, including more 'traditional' subjects such as programming languages, data processing, and systems analysis.

Although the book is intended to cover the IT components of BTEC and RSA courses, and professional courses such as CIPFA, AAT, and ICSA, it is hopefully also a 'good read'. If you want to find out about the whole field of IT – from how microchips work, through the latest developments in multimedia, to the automated factory and to social issues such as the likely impact of IT on employment – then read on.

*Roger Carter*
*Reader in Information Technology*
*The Buckinghamshire College*
*High Wycombe*

# 1
# The information revolution

## 1.1 The new age

I belong to the 1960s generation. At school in the 1950s, we were excited by the idea of being at the threshold of the atomic age and the space age. Favourite reading was Dan Dare, pilot of the future. Looking back now from the perspective of the 1990s, these ideas, and our reading material, seem rather quaint. Neither atomic energy nor space travel have had much of an impact on the world, except as deterrents to war.

What has had an enormous impact on the world since the 1950s is information processing. Most of the things we do have been revolutionized in one way or another by the new information processing technology. To give just a few examples:

- The music we listen to is often processed using modern computer-based equipment and stored in the form of information on magnetic tape or compact disc.
- The pictures we look at are shot with cameras incorporating information processing features which measure light and distances and then make automatic adjustments of lens aperture and focusing.
- The newspapers we read are produced from information keyed in, stored, and processed in electronic form.

Most aspects of our economy, from the music industry, TV and other parts of the leisure industry to manufacturing, banking, retailing, and defence, are now totally dependent upon modern information processing.

The age we live in turns out to be not the atomic age, nor the space age, but the information age.

## 1.2   How the information revolution began

Why did the atomic age and the space age fail to materialize? If we look back to other ages in man's history, such as
the stone age and the iron age, we see that they were based
on a low-cost and widely available technology: shaped flints
(called flint chips) in the case of the stone age, and iron
smelting in the case of the iron age. Atomic devices and
space vehicles are neither low cost nor widely available, and
so have not revolutionized our lives.

What no one foresaw in the 1950s was the invention, at
the start of the 1960s, of the silicon chip. This device, which
quickly became a low-cost mass-produced commodity, is
able to process large amounts of information at high speeds.
Besides being cheap and powerful, it is also very small –
about the size of a fingernail. In the 1950s, the equivalent
amount of processing power would have required a room-
sized computer with costs running into six figures. To
emphasize their smallness, silicon chips are also called
'microchips'. (This is a better name, since substances other
than silicon can now be used to produce chips.)

Today, if you buy a camera, or a washing machine, or a
TV, or a car, or indeed one of a host of other manufactured products, the chances are that it is controlled by a
microchip. Microchips inside computers now govern information processing in commercial and governmental organizations. There are few offices, factories, banks, or other
institutions that do not depend upon these ubiquitous
devices.

## 1.3   The impact of microchips

Flint chips revolutionized human societies and economies in
the stone age because they formed the basis of a range of
tools which extended the power of men's hands. This made
people much more productive. The microchips which are
revolutionizing our society and economy are extending the
powers of men's brains.

I've mentioned modern cameras as an example of the
impact of modern information processing. Taking snapshots
with 1950s-vintage cameras required the use of light meters,

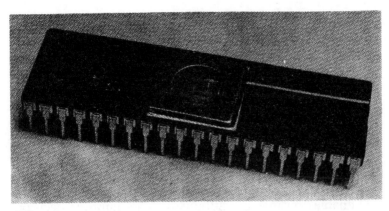

*Figure 1.1* A microchip

range finders, and fiddling with lens settings; with a modern microchip-controlled camera, in contrast, you just point and shoot. This means that:

- You have less to learn about the technicalities of taking photographs.
- Point-and-shoot is quick and easy compared to traditional methods with light meters and range finders.
- The quality will be higher, as human error in setting the aperture and focusing is eliminated.
- Freed of the technicalities, you can concentrate your attention on the composition of the picture.

The same kinds of advantages apply to other equipment that incorporates the information processing power of microchips. Nowhere is the result more plainly seen than in the office. Tasks which a few decades ago required armies of office workers can now be done automatically by computers under the control of a few people. This has not resulted in massive unemployment, any more than flint chips brought unemployment to the stone age. What happened then was that output increased, so that people had more food, clothing, and other necessities of life. Likewise today, the main impact of the microchip has been the production of far more information by the same number of workers.

What happened in factories in the past with the introduction of automation – i.e. enormous productivity increases –

is now happening in the office and other places where information is generated.

## 1.4  The information explosion

As a result of this revolution, a major difference between life today and life in the 1950s is the sheer volume of information that is now available:

- Huge quantities of *numerical and statistical information* produced by computer data processing systems. This enables businesses and governments improve decision-making and keep a better grip on their activities.
- Vast amounts of *textual information*, from newspapers and newsletters to reports and books. This is produced using computerized word processing and publishing systems.
- Enormous volumes of *information in the form of sound*, including music and the spoken word. Much of this is communicated electronically over the airwaves, cable, compact disc, and magnetic tape.
- A deluge of *information in the form of images*, in particular information communicated via TV.

On the face of it, these four forms of information are quite different. Statistical data, for example, seems far removed from pop music. In fact, these apparent differences spring from our perception of the information and the use we make of it rather than from the information itself. Today, microchips are being used to handle information in all these different forms, and multipurpose systems based on microchips capable of dealing with not only numerical data and text but also sound and images are commonplace.

## 1.5  The information factory

We don't often think of offices (and other places such as music and film studios where information is produced) as factories, but that is what they are. The same production principles apply to them as to factories, and microchip-based automation is having just as great an effect on them. We are all aware of the enormous strides that have been made in both the quantity and quality of manufactured goods over the last few decades. Similar strides are now being made in the production of information in offices and other information-handling areas. Information today is not only much more plentiful, it is, for the most part, of a higher quality.

We all know what 'quality' means when applied to goods produced in a factory: accurate tolerances, speedy delivery, reliability, and so on. Similar concepts apply to the production of information. By quality of information we mean:

- *Accuracy.* Microchips and computers not only process information very quickly, they don't make mistakes. So calculations of statistical and other numerical data are accurate. In the case of information in the form of sound or image 'accuracy' can mean more faithful reproduction of the original; in the case of books and other textual information, 'accuracy' includes correct spelling (helped by the use of automatic spell checkers in computer systems).
- *Timeliness.* With computers, calculations of statistical and other data are carried out very rapidly, so reports on a business's activities will be very timely. This contrasts with reports produced by manual methods, which could take months. Even the production of something like this book is much faster using computers, so that it is less out-of-date by the time it goes to press.
- *Relevance.* The message conveyed by the information may be trivial or irrelevant to the reader/listener/viewer; it may contain too much detail, or it may not have enough detail. Information technology can help here by its ability to store vast amounts of information and to allow rapid access to selected parts of it. Modern information-retrieval systems – including management information systems, hypertext systems, and computer-based training systems – all make use of IT techniques to tailor the message to the recipient's needs. These are described later in this book.
- *Presentation.* This is the most obvious aspect of 'quality'. In order to increase its impact, information should

be well presented. Modern information technology allows us to instantly convert tedious tables of figures to attractive charts and graphs, to print them via high-quality printers, or display them as slides or on a computer monitor. It also enables us to mix and control a variety of media such as video, audio, and computer output.

In today's information factory the microchip has not only revolutionized the volume of output, it has transformed the quality as well. This is true whether the information produced is in the form of numerical data, or text, or sound, or image.

## 1.6   The information processing operations

In a factory, the following sequence of operations is carried out:

- Raw materials are brought in and made available.
- They are processed by the equipment to produce the finished goods.
- The finished goods are stored in a convenient location, then withdrawn when required.
- They are transported to the customer.

The same series of operations are carried out in an 'information factory', whether an office or something like a sound studio. To illustrate this, let's take the example of information in the form of sound – music, in fact. For you to be able to listen to a piece of recorded music, the following operations must have been carried out:

1  First, the live music – the 'raw materials' – will have been *captured* using suitable input devices (i.e. microphones).
2  Next it will have been *processed* using mixing equipment to get the right balance, to incorporate effects, and so on.
3  Then it will have been *stored* on a master tape. Once

stored, it can be *retrieved* at any time, i.e. played back and/or copied.

4 Finally, it will have been *communicated* to you by copying it to cassette tapes or compact discs which you either bought and played on your own equipment or listened to on the radio.

These four operations – capture, processing, storage and retrieval, and communication – apply to the handling of any kind of information. If I took as an example the production of numerical information about a business's activities (e.g. its costs and its sales), or the production of something like this book, I would arrive at this same list of operations.

Take my phone, for example. This contains a microchip which will autodial many of the telephone numbers I use. (This not only saves me the bother of looking up numbers and dialling, it cuts out misdialling.) These are the operations that have to be carried out to use the autodial facility:

- To begin with, the phone has to *capture* the number I wish to store, so I have to key it in on the telephone keypad.
- Next it has to *store* this information, so I press the 'store' key. Later, when I wish to *retrieve* the number, I press the key marked 'memory'.
- The phone then *processes* the stored information by converting it to a code of electrical pulses understood by the telephone exchange.
- Finally it *communicates* the information by sending the pulses down the phone line.

## 1.7 Definition of information technology

I have likened the production of information to the production of goods in a factory. If I were to ask you to define what a factory is, you would probably end up with a definition that included the acquisition of raw materials, their processing, and the storage and distribution of the finished goods. You would also need to make some reference to the use of machines and equipment to carry out this process – for making a rabbit hutch at home using simple tools does not mean that your home is a factory!

If I asked you instead to define information technology, the only change you would need to make to this would be to replace 'raw materials' and 'finished goods' by terms such as 'data' and 'information'. Here's a simple definition:

> Information technology (IT for short) is the use of modern technology to aid the capture, processing, storage and retrieval, and communication of information, whether in the form of numerical data, text, sound, or image.

There are many more complicated definitions, but they all say much the same thing. Here's the one offered by the Northern Examination Association:

> Information technology is the study of information handling and its use in society by means of modern technology. This includes the acquisition, processing, storage and communication of information in any form by appropriate means. Within information technology there is an identifiable body of subject content, skills and activities. This common core is transferable, relevant to other curriculum areas and has wide application in society.

Note the reference to 'modern technology' in both these definitions. Traditional methods of information handling using simple tools – such as writing notes using pencil and paper – are excluded, just as making a rabbit hutch at home is excluded from our definition of a factory. Most IT devices (though not all) are controlled by microchips. These chips may be incorporated in the equipment itself (as in the case of my autodial telephone), or they may be incorporated in the computers which control the equipment.

## 1.8   Applications of IT

This section indicates the wide application of IT in modern society. Many of the devices and systems listed here are described later in this book.

- *The home*. Radio and TV broadcasting, and home video and audio systems, have had a major impact on our lives. Today, these systems increasingly incorporate microchips, and are able to process information not just in the form of sound and image but data and text also. Thus TV sets are used, for example, to pick up and display Ceefax and Oracle transmissions. Washing machines, microwave ovens, cookers, and other home appliances are now controlled by microchips. Quite new kinds of products, which would not have been possible without the microchip, are now commonplace – such as the digital watch, video games, the electronic musical keyboard, and the home computer.

  In the future, many of these home devices will probably be linked together and controlled by a computer. This means, for example, that if you are out for the day on a family trip and delayed home, you will be able to phone through to your computer and so reprogram the oven, set the video to record the programme you will otherwise miss, make sure the burglar alarm is on, close the curtains, and switch on the lights to simulate people at home.

- *The office*. Modern photocopiers, calculators, and typewriters are controlled by microchips. Most important of all, of course, is the computer, which is able to carry out all types of office task from writing letters and reports to producing charts and graphs and controlling projects.

- *The factory*. Nowadays, products are often designed using computer-aided design techniques. In the factory itself, the equipment and processes may be controlled by microchips. Even the warehousing of the finished products may be computer-controlled.

- *Transport and communications*. Telecommunications systems, including the telephone network, are increasingly computer-controlled, as are transport systems such as railways and the underground. Microchips are increasingly used in cars and other vehicles, and in the future may be connected via telecommunications links to traffic-control computers.

- *Education and training*. Computers and educational software are widely used in schools and colleges. Multimedia learning materials – such as video material stored on video disk or video tape and linked to computers to form interactive video systems – have been found to be very effective and are growing in popularity.

- *The arts.*   Computers are now being applied to all the main forms of art. They can synthesize music, to provide a wide range of musical sounds and effects, and they can instantly alter musical variables such as pitch, timbre, tempo, and loudness. Computer animation, which made possible a number of films of the Star Wars variety, is now becoming an art form in its own right. Computer graphics, video titling, and other techniques are also being widely used in TV and video production. Even painters can now use computer systems to compose their pictures electronically.

- *Retailing, law enforcement, and defence.*   In retailing, microprocessor-based point-of-sale systems are commonplace, and there are often links between these and the banking system, so that goods can be purchased by directly debiting the customer's account. In law enforcement, computers are being used to increase police efficiency in fighting crime. One of the biggest users of microprocessors is now the military, with its computerized battle-management systems, guided missiles, and other hardware.

This list is far from comprehensive, but it illustrates the extent of the impact of IT on our lives.

## 1.9   Analogue and digital systems

In the world of physics, the universe is seen to be made up of energy and matter. These can both be treated in two alternative ways: as waves, or as particles. Light, for example, travels in the form of light waves, but it is also true to say that it travels in the form of particles called photons. We *measure* waves – their amplitude, and their frequency – but we *count* particles.

These two quite different ways of dealing with the physical universe apply also to information handling:

- *Waves/particles.* In the traditional telephone system, for example, the electrical information that carries the speech travels in the form of waves, whereas in modern communications sytems it travels in the form of pulses (of electron particles).
- *Measuring/counting.* Kitchen scales of the traditional variety measure the weight of food by means of a pointer attached to a spring inside the scale; electronic scales, in contrast, carry out the task by counting, displaying the result on a digital readout. Traditional watches use a system of gears to measure the passage of time, whereas digital watches work by counting the oscillations of a quartz crystal.

We could give many other examples contrasting these two kinds of information-handling devices. The first type of device is referred to as *analogue*, the second as *digital* (since it is based on counting numerical digits). One of the major effects of the information revolution has been to replace our many analogue systems with digital ones. So we hear much today of the new digital audio systems, digital TV, digital communications systems, and so on.

There are two main reasons for this change:

1 Microchips, and therefore the devices that incorporate them, handle information in digital form. (See Chapter 2 for detail on this.) If you want to use computers to aid the production of music, for example, you must first convert the sound waves to digital electrical pulses in a wire.
2 Digital information can be stored and communicated without any degradation, whereas analogue information degrades. This degradation is very apparent when you make several generations of copies of an audio tape. Eventually, the quality becomes so poor that the copy is worthless. Compare this to information in digital form, for example data stored on a computer disk. You can make as many generations of copy as you like, and the final disk is still identical to the original.

The information in the case of the computer disk is stored as a series of magnetized spots on the disk. A particular location is either magnetized (representing the digit 1) or not magnetized (representing the digit 0). When you copy a disk, an identical series of 1s and 0s is produced on the copy – there is no possibility of a '1' being degraded to 0.99, as you would get in an analogue system. And although it is theoretically possible for a '1' to be copied to a '0' in error, various checking techniques can be applied to ensure that this does not happen.

(In the case of communications systems, digital data will degrade if the signal travels for a long distance without boosting. In this case the message may be completely scrambled – an effect that is sometimes observed with Ceefax or Oracle pages.)

Digital systems, then, offer the twin advantages of computer control and high quality. That's why audio, video, communications, and other systems are all going digital. An important by-product is that all forms of information, whether image, sound, or data, can be handled by the same equipment.

## 1.10   Systems theory

The information revolution has not only changed the way we live and the technology we use, it has also altered the way we think. Words such as 'input' and 'output', part of our everyday language now, are evidence of this. Increasingly, we think in a 'systems' way.

Systems theory – or *cybernetics* – was developed to provide a conceptual approach to modern engineering and IT systems. It has permeated much of our thinking, and is now applied to other types of system, such as biological systems and social systems. Like all good theories, the underlying idea is simple and elegant. A device such as a computer, or a social organization such as a business, or a living creature such as a human being, can be viewed as a 'black box' which converts inputs received from its environment to outputs transmitted to its environment. Control is exercised, not by monitoring what goes on inside the black box, but by monitoring the outputs that emerge from it, and adjusting the inputs in the event of undesirable output variations (see Figure 1.2).

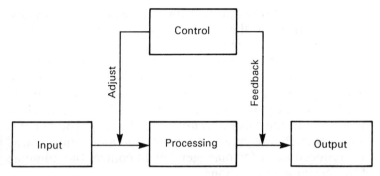

*Figure 1.2*   A system

To illustrate this, think about a simple engineering system, a central heating system:

- The 'black box' is the boiler and pump which heats the water and pumps it around the system.
- The inputs it receives from its environment are the gas and electricity needed to run the boiler and pump.
- The output to its environment is the heat released by the radiators into the rooms.
- Control is exercised by the thermostat, which monitors the heat in the room, and adjusts the inputs (i.e. switches the boiler on or off) if the heat falls below or rises above the required temperature range.

These same concepts can be applied to the way in which a department of a business is run. In this case the department is the 'black box', the inputs are the staff, the equipment and materials, and so on, and the outputs are what the department produces. In control of the department is a manager. If he (or she) manages in the traditional way, using non-systems thinking, he will exercise control by keeping a watchful eye on the way in which his staff work, ensuring that they have their heads down, conform to the laid-down procedures, and so on.

The more up-to-date systems approach to control is to set the department's output targets, and then let the staff get on with the job. The manager is not concerned with how the 'black box' works – how the targets are met is up to the staff – the manager needs to take action only if the targets are not met. This action will involve adjusting the inputs, e.g. strengthening the staff by giving more training or improving the equipment.

It is clear that the systems approach needs careful planning of output targets, as these must be realistic. It also means setting up procedures to allow the manager to monitor the output by producing feedback on the work of the section in the form of *reports* (see below). The benefits gained, though, are greater efficiency and motivation as well as a reduced need for management to control the minutiae of the business's operations.

Turning now to the business as a whole, this too can be regarded as a system under the control of the board of directors or top management. Control is exercised by comparing the profit generated by the business (its main output) against the level of profit anticipated by the business plan, and issuing from time to time short-term budgets to keep the business on course (see Figure 1.3). The feedback reports used by top management to control the business will include profit and loss reports, sales reports, and other measures of overall business performance.

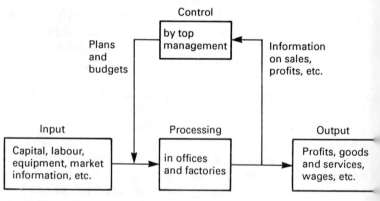

*Figure 1.3*  The systems view of a business

## 1.11  Output standards

Controlling a system, then, requires that the outputs of that system have been carefully planned and precisely stated. A controller must be able to check whether his or her system has or has not achieved the plan. If the plan is stated in vague terms he will often be left in doubt, for he will not be able to make a precise comparison between the performance (as measured in the reports of the type described above) and the plan. The result will be that he may not know whether any input adjustments are required (overtime working, training, etc.), and his system's outputs will vary from what is required, to the detriment of other systems that depend upon it.

Systems theory emphasizes the need to lay down precise and realistic standards (targets) expressed in terms of *quantity, quality*, and *time*. In other words, the plan for a system should state how much is to be produced within a given time, and at what quality. The plan should be stated in quantitative (i.e. numerical) terms, which means putting a precise value on the amount to be produced and on the quality standards.

The output standards of a system must be realistic. If they are too easy to achieve then the system will be working below its capacity and resources of manpower and equipment will be underutilized. If they are too difficult, then the system will not be able to achieve its planned output, which will adversely affect other dependent systems, as well as affecting the morale of people working within the system.

## 1.12   The information processing system

Most systems are made up of a number of *subsystems*. The human body – itself a system – is made up of a digestive system, a nervous system, a lung system, and so on. A business contains many subsystems, like sales, purchasing, stores, etc. Each subsystem has as its environment – from which it receives inputs and to which it gives outputs – other subsystems within the overall system as well as the overall system's environment. One of the subsystems within a business will be its information processing system.

The information processing system receives a variety of data inputs from other subsystems within the business, as well as data inputs from customers and suppliers in the business's environment. From those inputs it produces a variety of outputs. These outputs are of two sorts:

- *Transaction documents.* Invoices sent to customers, purchase orders sent to suppliers, works orders sent to the business's factory, and so on. Large numbers of these documents are produced (perhaps in electronic form, displayed on computer screens). They are the crucial 'paperwork' without which the business would rapidly come to a halt.
- *Reports.* Profit and loss reports generated for top management, sales reports generated for the marketing manager, scrap reports generated for the factory manager, and so on. These reports summarize many hundreds of thousands of individual transactions into a few key figures, so giving management an overall perspective of the business's performance. Compared to the large number of transaction documents, relatively few reports are generated, but it is these documents that provide feedback on how the business is doing and so enable management to exercise control over it.

Computers have proved invaluable in business not only because they can automate the production of transaction documents, but also because they can produce accurate and up-to-the-minute reports. Before the days of computers, armies of clerks were needed to produce these summaries and analyses of the business's performance, which were therefore expensive to produce, often weeks or months late, and frequently incomplete. Because of the patchiness of this information, management could not properly control the business, which resulted in reduced competitiveness and reduced profitability.

One of the valuable results of the systems approach is the emphasis that is now placed on *exception reporting*. Since the manager of a system only needs to take action when the output deviates from the planned figures, there is no point giving a detailed report on those areas in which performance does not deviate from but matches the plan. That would cause the manager not only to waste time reading unnecessary information, but it might also result in him or her missing the important information that requires a response.

Performance reports should clearly give deviations only. Computers are able to automatically do this.

A well-designed information processing system today can produce as many performance reports as are required by the various managers in an organization, tailored to meet their precise requirements and produced at exactly the frequency they need.

## 1.13 Sub-optimization

Each system controller will try to maximize the performance of his or her own system. For example, the data processing manager will want the latest, fastest and most powerful equipment so that his department can process its work as rapidly as possible. That way he gains the greatest kudos in the organization. The factory manager will have similar aims. After all, no one wants to appear to be doing a second-rate job.

The organization has limited resources, however, and if it gives the DP manager everything he wants then the factory manager may get very little. The organization will then be able to process its data very efficiently, but it won't do so well at producing goods. By maximizing his own performance the DP manager is actually working to the detriment of the organization as a whole. The organization's limited resources have not been shared out in the best way, and the organization is unable to achieve optimum performance. This is called *sub-optimization*.

Top management obviously has to look at the outputs it expects from the organization as a whole, and decide how best to distribute its resources amongst the subsystems in order to achieve those outputs. This is the principle of budgeting. Information processing obviously has an important role to play in the organization, but only top management can decide how much of its resources should be allocated to it.

The sub-optimization issue arises because the aims and the needs of one subsystem may conflict to some extent with those of another. To avoid sub-optimization it is necessary to bring subsystems that do conflict in this way together, placing them under a common superior.

## 1.14　System boundaries

A system is said to be *bounded* by its inputs. These are, if you like, the 'interface' between it and its environment. When an information system is being designed, the first thing to decide is what its outputs should be, and what inputs are needed to produce these outputs. System boundaries are often movable: the system designer might wish to extend the boundaries of a system i.e. increase the number of outputs and therefore the number of inputs. (This will clearly reduce the boundaries of other systems by removing outputs and inputs from them.) Or he may wish to restrict the boundaries by breaking the system down into a number of subsystems, each with a more limited number of outputs and inputs.

When computers were first introduced into business in the 1960s the systems that they were designed to automate were very large. They had to be, as the computers themselves were large and expensive and could only be effectively used as a central resource for large-scale data processing activities such as accounting and stock control. Today, small inexpensive personal computers are taking over much of the business's information processing. Instead of being a centralized facility, they are spread throughout the business, handling information on a departmental or sectional basis. Information systems therefore tend to be smaller and more informal – in other words, their boundaries are much more restricted.

The advantages of a large system include the fact that many users can share the same data, and that procedures are determined centrally and are consistent throughout the organization. The advantages of small systems include the fact that the users themselves can set up their own systems to meet their own requirements, rather than have someone else's ideas imposed on them, and systems can be much more flexible.

So when designing an information processing system, the first task is to define what its boundaries (i.e. its outputs and inputs) should be. Should it be restricted to serving a single section, or should it be much bigger, with outputs to several departments and correspondingly wide inputs?

Information has been called the life-blood of a business.

From it, all the transaction documents that the business needs to carry on its work are produced, as well as the performance reports that management needs to properly control the business. The design of the information processing systems are obviously of crucial importance, and can affect not only the efficiency and control of the entire organization, but also the way in which departments work.

## 1.15  Systems analysis

The design of information systems is called *systems analysis*, and is carried out by *systems analysts*. The detailed implementation of these designs will normally be carried out by other people in the organization, including computer programmers. The work of systems analysts, programmers, and other data processing personnel is described in Chapter 9.

Systems analysis involves the investigation and analysis of an information system, and will have as its result:

- A specification of the inputs and the outputs of the system. In the case of an invoicing system, for example, this specification will include the numbers of customers and products that are involved, numbers of transactions, and the reports that are required.
- A specification of the data that needs to be stored in the system, and the structure of the files that are to hold the data. These specifications are called *data dictionaries* and *file formats* respectively.
- A specification of the computer hardware and software that will be required.

It is the task of computer programmers to write the programs needed to implement the system. Computer programming is covered in Chapter 4.

# 2
# Computers

## 2.1 What is a computer?

A computer is a device which enables you to process information (1) automatically and (2) in accordance with instructions that you give it.

(1) means that it can carry out the capture–process–store–communicate sequence described in Chapter 1 all by itself, or at least with the minimum of human intervention. It does this by means of *hardware*, i.e. information capture, processing, storage, and communicating devices, linked together electronically.

(2) means that it can be adapted to carry out almost any kind of information processing task, whether word processing or stock control. It does this by means of *software*, i.e. sets of instructions or *programs* which control these hardware devices so that they carry out the required operations on the information.

In this chapter and the next we look at the various pieces of hardware. In subsequent chapters we turn our attention to the software.

## 2.2 Computer hardware

The hardware of a computer system consists of the devices listed below. They are all described in this chapter and the next.

- Input devices to capture the information, such as the keyboard, mouse, microphone, or scanner.

- The central processing unit (CPU), containing the *arithmetic logic unit* (ALU), which carries out the logical and arithmetic computations that lie at the heart of computing (see below), and the *control unit*, which executes commands typed at the keyboard or stored in software.
- Storage is split into short-term *memory*, using microchips inside the computer, which hold data and programs while processing is being carried out, and long-term *storage*, normally using magnetic disks.
- Output devices for communicating the results of the processing, such as a printer, monitor, or loudspeaker.
- I should also mention the circuitry linking these various devices, consisting of 8, 16, or 32 strands of parallel wire, called *buses*, along which all the bits that make up each item of information travel in parallel.

We can represent the computer hardware by the usual sort of systems diagram, though it is helpful to represent storage by a separate box linked to the CPU (see Figure 2.1).

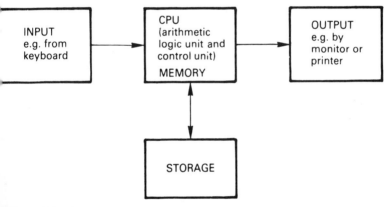

*Figure 2.1*  A computer system

## 2.3  Microprocessors

I'll start by describing microprocessors (microchips), as these lie at the heart of computers and other information processing devices. The CPU inside a modern computer will consist of one or more of these chips, which contain the logic circuitry needed to perform computations. A chip is packaged in a holder containing the electrical connections needed to link it to other devices such as a keyboard (see Figure 1.1). Microchips which act as memory are described later in this chapter.

In essence, a microprocessor works in the same way as the rooms full of glass 'thermionic' valves which made up the CPUs of the earliest computers. Each valve was a switch which could be turned OFF by applying a strong negative electrical charge to it, or ON by applying a weak electrical charge. If it was ON a current could flow through it, if it was OFF no current could flow.

Instead of thermionic valves, which were bulky, unreliable, and expensive, we now have an alternative type of electrically operated switch, the tiny transistor. A transistor is shown in diagrammatic form in Figure 2.2.

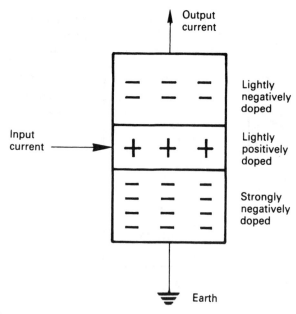

*Figure 2.2*   A transistor

A transistor consists of three layers of doped silicon, i.e. silicon to which a small amount of another substance has been added. Doped silicon is a *semiconductor*. This means that under certain circumstances it will conduct electricity, otherwise it won't. Silicon can be positively doped, i.e. the added substance has fewer valence electrons than pure silicon, or negatively doped, i.e. the added substance has more valence electrons. In either case, an electric current can flow under the right conditions.

A strong current applied to the central positively doped layer in the transistor allows a current to flow between the two negatively doped layers, but a nil or weak current will prevent its flow. In this way the transistor acts like a switch.

A microprocessor is made up of many thousands of such transistors, linked to each other by microscopic circuitry etched into the surface of the chip.

### 2.4   How a microprocessor handles information

The old-fashioned thermionic valve and the modern transistor are said to be *bistable*, because they can be in only one of two states, in this case either ON or OFF. Other devices used in computers and IT equipment are also bistable. For example:

- A spot on the surface of storage devices such as magnetic disks or tapes can be either magnetized or demagnetized.
- A hole position on paper tape can be either punched or not punched.
- A spot on the surface of a compact disc can either have a pit burnt in it or not.

This means that microchips and other IT devices store information as sequences of ON/OFF switches, or sequences of magnetized/demagnetized spots, or sequences of holes/ no-holes. If we call an ON switch (or a magnetized spot, or a hole) 1, and an OFF switch (or demagnetized spot, or no-hole) 0, then all information must be broken down into sequences of 1s and 0s to be handled by a computer or other microprocessor-based equipment.

For example, when you type the letter A on a computer keyboard, it is converted to the following sequence of eight 1s and 0s:

01000001

The letter B is converted to 01000010, the letter C to 01000011, the letter D to 01000100, and so on.

To reach the CPU, a 1 becomes a strong pulse of electricity travelling down the wire linking the keyboard to the rest of the computer, and a 0 becomes a weak pulse. When they reach the CPU, each weak pulse switches a transistor OFF, while a strong pulse turns a transistor ON. In this way a letter pressed on the keyboard is converted to an ON/OFF switch sequence inside the computer.

Pocket calculators work in a similar way, as does every other microprocessor-based device. When you use drawing software to draw a picture on the computer screen, the computer converts your artistry into sequences of 0s and 1s which give screen coordinates, colours, and other information about each point of your picture. If you speak into a speech recognition device (see Chapter 3), your words are converted to sequences of 0s and 1s.

These 0s and 1s are, of course, numerical digits, which is why computers and other IT devices are said to be *digital*. In the past, some computers were not digital, but instead represented data as varying voltages. These were called *analogue*. I compared digital and analogue devices in Chapter 1 on page 10. Modern microprocessors are so cheap and powerful that almost all IT devices are now digital.

## 2.5   Binary numbers

Each of the sequences of 0s and 1s described in the last section is an item of numerical data. Back at school, you probably met numbers that use just the two digits 0 and 1: they are called *binary numbers*. They relate to ordinary decimal numbers as follows:

| Decimal | Binary |
|---------|--------|
| zero    | 0      |
| one     | 1      |
| two     | 10     |
| three   | 11     |
| four    | 100    |
| five    | 101    |

and so on. Can you discern the pattern in this?

The digits 0 and 1 that make up a binary number are called *b*inary dig*its*, or *bits* for short. In most computers, information is handled in groups of eight bits, which is why there are eight 0s and 1s in the binary representations of A, B, C, and D above. A group of eight bits is called a *byte*, which may be short for 'by eight'.

As I said earlier, microprocessors contain many thousands of transistors, and magnetic disks and other IT equipment also contain huge numbers of bistable devices. To cope with quantities of this magnitude we use the following terms:

- Kb or Kbyte (short for *kilobyte*), meaning about 1,000 bytes (1024, to be exact).
- Mb or Mbyte (short for *megabyte*), meaning about 1,000,000 bytes (1024 Kb, to be exact).
- Gb or Gbyte (short for *gigabyte*), meaning 1,000,000,000 bytes (1024 Mb, to be exact).

## 2.6 Microprocessors and logic

(The next sections are slightly more technical than other parts of the book. If you wish, you can omit them and turn straight to the section 'Microprocessors and computers' on page 32.)

Computers operate according to the rules of logic. That's why the heart of the CPU is called the 'arithmetic logic unit' (ALU). To this end, the glass valves in the earliest computers, and the transistors in modern microprocessors, are organized into what are called *logic gates*. These enable the microprocessor to perform the logical operations AND, OR, and NOT. The significance of this is that by combining these operations, the microprocessor can carry out arithmetic computations on the information that is fed into it.

So to explain how microprocessors compute, we need to look into the rules governing logical operators. They come from Boolean algebra, a branch of mathematics developed by Boole in the first part of the last century. These rules go something like this.

Any proposition can be true or false. For example, the proposition *Ann is going to the party* is either true or false, as is the proposition *Barbara is going to the party*. We'll call the first proposition A and the second B. We'll also use the number 1 to represent true and the number 0 to represent false. So in the language of Boolean algebra,

A = 1 means: *Ann is going to the party* is true
A = 0 means: *Ann is going to the party* is false.

Similary,

B = 1 means: *Barbara is going to the party* is true
B = 0 means: *Barbara is going to the party* is false.

## 2.7    The AND operator

We can combine the propositions like those in the above example using the logical operators, AND, OR, and NOT. For example,

A AND B = 1 means: *Ann is going* and *Barbara is going* are both true
A AND B = 0 means: *Ann is going* and *Barbara is going* are not both true, i.e. either one or the other, or both, are false.

We can represent statements like this by a *truth table*. A truth table for this example shows the effect of different values of A and B on the values taken by A AND B:

| A | B | A AND B |
|---|---|---------|
| 0 | 0 | 0 |
| 0 | 1 | 0 |
| 1 | 0 | 0 |
| 1 | 1 | 1 |

The first line of this table means:

If *Ann is going* is false, and if *Barbara is going* is false, then *Ann and Barbara are going* is false.

## 2.8 The AND gate

Figure 2.3 shows a simple electrical circuit which performs the AND operations described above. It is called an
AND gate. The switches at A and B in this circuit are
mechanical devices called solenoids, and the lamp in the
circuit is ON when a current flows, and OFF when it does
not flow. (In a microchip, each switch in an AND gate is a
transistor).

An electrical current in wire A closes the switch at A, and
an electrical current in wire B closes the switch at B. In
order to complete the circuit and allow the current marked
X to flow from the battery to the lamp, both switches have
to be closed, i.e. there has to be a current in wire A and in
wire B. If either one of these wires has no current flowing in
it, then one of the switches will be open and no current will
flow through the lamp.

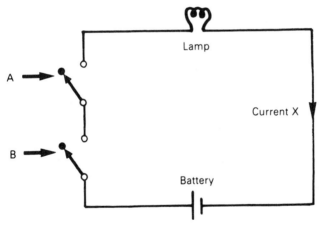

*Figure 2.3* An AND gate

Using 1 to represent the flow of current and 0 to represent
the absence of current, we can draw up a truth table showing
the values of X for different values of A and B. If you try
this, you will see that the truth table is identical to that
produced in the last section for the AND operator, and
proves that this circuit correctly represents the action of that
operator.

## 2.9    The OR operator

The second logical operator is OR. Using the party example
from the previous sections,

> A OR B = 1 means: *Ann is going (to the party)* is
>                         true, or *Barbara is going* is
>                         true, or both are true
> A OR B = 0 means: none of the above are true, i.e.
>                         both propositions are false.

Again, we can draw up a truth table to represent this:

| A | B | A OR B |
|---|---|--------|
| 0 | 0 | 0 |
| 0 | 1 | 1 |
| 1 | 0 | 1 |
| 1 | 1 | 1 |

The electrical circuit shown in Figure 2.4 reproduces the
effect of this table. In this circuit, the switches A and B are
in parallel, and current X will flow if either A or B (or both)
are closed.

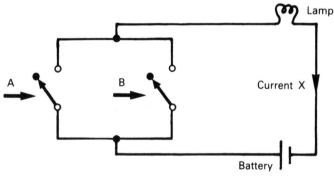

*Figure 2.4*    An OR gate

## 2.10    The NOT operator

The third logical operator is NOT. In the example we have
used already, NOT A means *Ann is not going (to the party)*

and NOT B means *Barbara is not going*. So if *Ann is going* is true, then NOT A is false. The truth table representing this is:

| A | NOT A |
|---|-------|
| 0 | 1 |
| 1 | 0 |

In electronics, a NOT gate consists of a special sort of switch which closes and so makes a circuit when no current is applied to it, and opens and so breaks the circuit when there is a current.

### 2.11 Combining logical operators

We can combine these logical operators (and the circuits which represent them) in any number of ways. Staying with the party example, Colin may decide to go to the party if:

(A OR B) AND NOT (A AND B) = 1

This means he will go to the party if

A OR B = 1, i.e. if Ann or Barbara go, AND if
NOT (A AND B) = 1, i.e. if they don't both go.

So he'll go with one or the other but not both.

The truth table for this can be built up in stages. The first stage is to construct intermediate values for A OR B and NOT (A AND B). The stage combines these two intermediate results using the AND operator.

| A | B | A OR B | NOT (A AND B) | (A OR B) AND NOT (A AND B) |
|---|---|--------|---------------|----------------------------|
| 0 | 0 | 0 | 1 | 0 |
| 0 | 1 | 1 | 1 | 1 |
| 1 | 0 | 1 | 1 | 1 |
| 1 | 1 | 1 | 0 | 0 |

## 2.12   Arithmetic and logic

Most of the work done by a computer involves arithmetic calculations. The basic task in this arithmetic is the addition of the two binary numbers 0 and 1. If A and B can each take either of these two values, the resulting values of A + B will be as follows:

| A | B | A + B | Explanation |
|---|---|---|---|
| 0 | 0 | 0 | Zero + zero = zero |
| 0 | 1 | 1 | Zero + one = one |
| 1 | 0 | 1 | One + zero = one |
| 1 | 1 | 10 | One + one = two (i.e. 10 in binary) |

The last column of this table, which shows the results of the addition, really consists of two columns: a two's column (i.e. 10 in binary) and a units column. So we could rewrite the table like this:

| A | B | A + B | |
|---|---|---|---|
| | | twos | units |
| 0 | 0 | 0 | 0 |
| 0 | 1 | 0 | 1 |
| 1 | 0 | 0 | 1 |
| 1 | 1 | 1 | 0 |

Notice that the two's column is identical to the results column of the A AND B truth table on page 26. The units column is the same as the results column of the (A OR B) AND NOT (A AND B) table in the last section.

This means that we can use logical operators, and therefore logic gates, to produce these two columns, and therefore to carry out binary calculations.

## 2.13   Logic circuits

Logic gates, shown as the simple electrical circuits on earlier pages in this chapter, therefore lie at the heart of all computing. As you have learned, these gates consist of switches connected up in various ways. In a microprocessor,

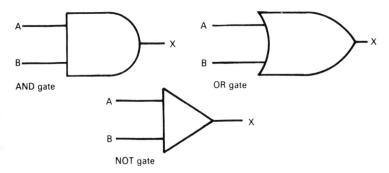

*Figure 2.5*   Symbols used for AND, OR, and NOT gates

each switch is a transistor, and a gate is therefore a simple circuit containing two or more transistors.

Rather than draw these circuits each time we wish to show an AND, OR, or NOT gate, it is much easier to use symbols. These are shown in Figure 2.5. Figure 2.6 shows a circuit called a 'half-adder gate' which produces the (A OR B) AND NOT (A AND B) column of the above truth table. (If you study this circuit, you will see that it does indeed represent this combination of logical operators.) As you learned in the last section, it is this combination of gates that carries out the basic task of addition.

There are other kinds of circuits used in the arithmetic logic units of computers, but they are all based upon the logical operators described in the previous sections, and consist of various combinations of the AND, OR, and NOT gates.

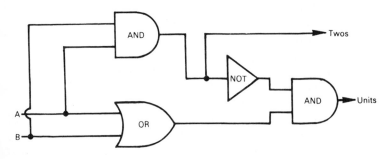

*Figure 2.6*   A half-adder gate

## 2.14   Microprocessors and computers

Any suitable type of switch can be used to build up the logic gate circuits used in the central processing units (CPUs) of computers. However, because many thousands are required to construct circuits for even the simplest computer, it is important that they should be small, reliable, cheap, and consume little power. Back in the 1940s and 1950s, there were very few computers, and those that existed were very large, expensive, and unreliable. This was because glass valves were used as switches inside their CPUs. The development of the transistor, used in today's microprocessors, brought about the revolution in switch technology needed for the spread of computing.

In the future, other types of switching device may prove viable. Some institutions are currently working on optical computers, using pulses of laser light instead of pulses of electrons to communicate the 0s and 1s of binary code. By constructing optical AND, OR and NOT gates they have demonstrated the feasibility of such computers, and their potential advantages are apparent when you consider that:

- No electrical wires will be needed, which will reduce the cost.
- Their speed will surpass that of electronic computers, as the information will travel at the speed of light.

However, optical computers have a long way to go to catch up with the high volume and low-cost production of microprocessors, and the present-day type of computer, using microprocessors as CPUs, will certainly reign supreme up to the end of this century.

There are a number of different microprocessor designs ('architectures') used for computer CPUs. Some, such as the Motorola 68000 series of microchips, contain an arrangement of logic circuits more suited for graphical applications, and so are used on the Apple Macintosh, the Atara ST, and the Amiga computers. Others, such as the Intel 80x86 series of chips, are more suitable for processing numerical data and text, and are used on the successors to the original IBM PC. Having said that, the latest generations of such chips are so powerful that there is little practical difference in their respective abilities to handle graphical or numerical applications, and the Apple Macintosh and the IBM PC's successors now run very similar software. If a software package proves a major success on one system, it's not long before it is converted to run on the other.

The most popular makes of CPU chips are described in the sections below. Each new generation may contain several times as many transistors as its predecessors, indicative of the fact that it has a greater number of and more complex logic circuits. Amongst other things, these enable it to:

- Carry out operations at higher speeds.
- Perform calculations to more significant figures (i.e. a higher degree of accuracy).
- Directly address more memory (and therefore support more complex software).

An important factor which affects all these is the number of bits that the CPU is able to process simultaneously. In the 1970s, the standard was 8-bit CPUs, whereas today it is 32-bits. This implies not only many more transistors in today's microprocessors, but also many more parallel wires in the data buses (cables) inside the computer. To keep costs down, some computers contain 32-bit chips but 16-bit data buses, i.e. the chips process data 32 bits at a time, but communicate data only 16 bits at a time. (This kind of restriction will disappear if optical computers become a reality.)

## 2.15 The Z80 microprocessor

This microchip, manufactured by Zilog, was the main CPU used in microcomputers in the 1970s and early 1980s. It is still used today in some low-priced computers such as the Amstrad PCW word processor. An enormous amount of business software has been written for computers which use this chip, and much of it is very cheap or even free.

The Z80 is, however, an 8-bit chip, and therefore of limited power. It is slow, and able to access only 64 Kbytes of memory. The result is that software running on Z80-

based computers is no match for the kind of thing that is now available on more up-to-date machines.

## 2.16   The 680x0 family of microprocessors

These are 32-bit microprocessors from Motorola. They appeared in the mid-1980s, and are used on computers which are strong on graphics such as the Apple Macintosh, the Atari ST, and the Amiga. The original chip, used on the first Apple Mac, was the 68000, the latest model (at the time of writing) is the 68040.

These chips are fast, and able to access many Gigabytes of memory.

## 2.17   The 80x86 family of microprocessors

These microprocessors, from Intel, are the most widely used, being the ones adopted by the IBM PC and its successors. 'Clones' of these chips are also available from other manufacturers. Most PCs today, whether 'compatibles' from the likes of Toshiba, Tandon, Olivetti, and Amstrad, or PS/2 machines from IBM itself, use these chips. In future I shall use the term 'PC' to mean personal computers of this type, as distinct from other microcomputers such as the Apple Macintosh.

The 8086 chip, used on earlier models of the IBM PC (at the beginning of the 1980s), was a 16-bit chip. It was therefore faster than the Z80 (which it effectively replaced), and could access 640K of memory. When the IBM PC first appeared, all business software on microcomputers was designed to run within 64K, and the potential to access ten times this amount seemed more than generous. Today, it seems paltry.

In the mid-1980s IBM produced a more advanced version of the PC called the AT (see page 48). This boasted the latest 32-bit 80286 chip which was capable, in theory, of accessing many Megabytes of memory (32 Mb in fact). Unfortunately, the operating system used on PCs limited it to 640K (see Chapter 5), and in any case the chip itself turned out to be 'brain damaged' and not capable of fulfilling these expectations. Today, the much more powerful 80386 and 80486 chips are with us, with none of these memory limitations. At the time of writing the operating system still restricts memory access, but operating environments such as Windows break the 640K memory barrier (see Chapter 5).

During the 1980s, Intel chips gradually came to dominate the computer market. At the time of writing (late 1990), they account for some 40% of the market, and many analysts reckon that by the end of the century they will account for over 80%.

## 2.18   RISC microprocessors

In most CPUs, the control unit can handle a wide range of instructions. Most of these instructions are, however, infrequently used. RISC stands for *reduced instruction set computer*, and in RISC microprocessors the control unit is only able to handle the 20% most frequently used instructions. The remaining 80%, when needed, can be obtained by combining two or more of the instructions which are available. The design of RISC chips is such that the frequently used instructions are carried out very rapidly, far faster than on conventional chips. (A conventional chip is a 'complex instruction set computer', or CISC.)

The first microcomputer using RISC technology was the Acorn Archimedes, launched in Britain in 1987. Costing under £1000, this machine ran several times faster than other contemporary microcomputers, and was able to run applications involving intensive processing, such as graphics applications, at a speed never before seen in computers in this price range.

Today, RISC chips are available from both Intel and Motorola. Intel's main RISC chip, the i860, is compatible with its 80x86 chip series, and so can be incorporated in standard PCs. Its latest chip in the 80x86 series, the 80586 (not yet in production at the time of writing), will incorporate RISC technology. Also, new chips are available which incorporate both RISC and CISC technologies. Motorola's new 68040 processor incorporates both, and computers that use this are able to run at very high speeds.

## 2.19　The transputer

Short for *transistor computer*, the transputer contains, on a single chip, both the CPU and some memory, as well as communications channels to link it to other transputers. It is a RISC chip, so processing is very fast, and the fact that transputers can be linked means that they can process instructions in parallel.

The type of processing carried out in conventional computers is called *serial processing*. In this, the instructions contained in a program are carried out one after the other. This works well enough in office administration applications such as word processing and record keeping, which make relatively light demands of the CPU, but it is quite inadequate for very heavy processing tasks such as image recognition or speech recognition (see later).

To illustrate the problem, imagine how you would get on if you tried to recognize a face by breaking it down into a series of points and examining each in turn (i.e. serially). The task would take ages. What the brain does, in fact, is to examine each point simultaneously, so that you are able to instantly recognize the face. This is called *parallel processing*.

Because the transputer is a parallel processing device, any equipment that is based upon it will be able to operate more like the human brain, capable of carrying out the kind of complex recognition tasks that we take in our stride. The hope is that the next generation of IT equipment will be able to recognize and act upon speech, drawn images, handwritten instructions, and so on, as readily as we can.

## 2.20　Neural networks

Neural networks attempt to take computing even closer to the human brain. Even with parallel processing, computers are vastly outperformed by the brain at tasks such as image recognition. On the face of it, this is surprising, since current computers process data about a million times faster than the brain!

The reason is that the brain is able to learn from experience. In effect, it uses its experiences to build up generalized sets of rules, and then uses these to discern the essential characteristics in a mass of otherwise irrelevant data. This is what allows it to recognize instantly a face, a voice, an object, etc. What happens at the physical level in the brain is that successive experiences of a similar type build up and strengthen particular neurons. (Neurons are the filament-like tissue that carry electrical pulses of data in the brain.)

Neural networks are an attempt to mimic this learning activity of the brain. They consist of layers of simulated neurons on a silicon chip. The connections between these and the input and output nodes on the chip are strengthened or weakened according to the 'experiences' of the chip. Alternatively, neural networks can be software simulations running on conventional computers – these are much cheaper, but much slower than using specially-built chips.

To use a neural network, you first have to train it by repeatedly inputting samples of information it has to recognize, 'telling' it what that information is by indicating what its outputs should be. Eventually it builds up its internal connections so that it can reliably produce the desired output from other samples of information. In this way you can, for example, train a network to recognize letters of the alphabet written in a variety of hands. You present it with a series of a, b, c, etc., indicating at the same time the appropriate sequence of bits that correspond to each.

Neural networks are starting to be used in a variety of applications, including checking airport baggage for explosives and weapons, listening to car engines to spot defects, and picking out trends in financial trading data.

## 2.21  Digital signal processors

Digital signal processors (DSPs) are used in voice recognition systems (page 59), computer video applications such as interactive compact disc (page 169), complex mathematical calculations, music synthesis, as well as in more standard bits of equipment such as disk controllers and modems. They allow the high speed processing of digital signals from audio, video, and other sources.

DSPs are microchips optimized to carry out, at high speeds and with a high degree of accuracy, complex numerical calculations. They incorporate a number of enhancements to increase the processing speed. These may include dual arithmetic logic units, separate program and data memories, and high-speed memory access. This makes them suitable for numerically-intensive processing applications such as those listed above.

The first high-speed DSP was produced by AT&T in 1978. Since then Motorola, Texas Instruments, and others have produced DSPs, and these chips are now incorporated in a wide range of devices.

## 2.22   Processing speeds

The main way in which a computer's power is judged is the speed at which it runs. This depends upon two factors:

*   The speed of its internal clock, measured in millions of cycles per second (megahertz, or MHz for short).
*   The average number of clock cycles it requires to execute an instruction.

For example, a PC with an 80386 chip may have a clock speed of 20 or 25 MHz and will require about 4.5 clock cycles to perform an instruction. By dividing the clock speed by the number of cycles per instruction you can see that this gives a processing speed of around 5 million instructions per second (MIPS). (Compare this with the human brain – its neurons conduct electrical pulses at the frequency of about 1 kilohertz, which is snail-like in comparison.)

The purpose of the internal clock is to ensure that all the devices in the computer act in unison. It does this by sending electrical pulses through the system. The speed at which the clock is able to run is limited not only by the speed of the CPU but also the speed of the other components. So replacing an 8086 processor in an old PC by an 80386 processor does not mean that the PC will be able to run at 20 or 25 MHz.

The original IBM PC with its 8086 chip supported a clock speed of 4.77 MHz. To execute the average instruction required about 15 clock cycles, so its processing speed was 0.3 MIPS. The latest PCs using the 80486 chip have clock speeds of 30 or 35 MHz and execute an instruction in just over 2 clock cycles, giving a processing speed of around 15 MIPS. The i860 RISC chip has a clock speed of around 40 MHz and executes about 1 instruction per clock cycle, giving a processing speed of around 40 MIPS – about 130 times as fast as the original PC!

For much office software, e.g. character-based word processing and record keeping, the internal processing speed of the computer may not be very important, because this kind of software does not make heavy demands of the processor (i.e. it involves relatively few instructions per period of time). On the other hand, graphics software, speech processing, and some engineering and mathematical applications, make heavy demands on the processor and so are best run on fast computers.

Increasingly, standard office applications such as word processing are being run within graphical environments such as 'Windows' (see Chapter 5), and fast PCs, preferably based on the 80386 processor or above, are best for this. In fact, the PC world seems to be splitting into two camps, those with slower and cheaper computers running character-based software, and those with the more expensive models running graphics-based software within the Windows environment. As I shall explain later, for certain applications a graphics environment is highly desirable; however, for many run-of-the-mill office applications there is little point in using this environment and, indeed, certain advantages in remaining in the character-based world.

## 2.23 Computer memory

'Memory' is an area of storage within the computer where programs and data are held ready for processing by the CPU. The significant feature of memory, compared to disk storage, is that the CPU can access it at extremely high speeds, and any delays caused by moving data in and out of memory are therefore minimized. When you 'load' a file from disk, you are in fact copying it into an area of memory. However, compared to disk, memory is expensive and limited. The typical PC has less than 4 Mbyte of memory, but 40, 80, or 120 Mbyte of hard disk capacity, and access to an indefinite number of floppy disks.

Computer memory is of two types, *RAM* and *ROM*.

## 2.24   Random access memory

Random access memory, or RAM, is a temporary store for holding programs and data loaded from disk, or typed at the keyboard, or input from some other device. The term 'random access' means that the data can be picked out of the memory in any order, and contrasts with 'sequential access', which is the kind of access you get with magnetic tape and some other storage devices, where the data has to be read in sequence, starting at the beginning and working through to the end.

Nowadays, a RAM device is normally a silicon chip, made up of thousands of tiny (transistor) switches, each of which can be either ON or OFF, and so represent a binary digit (1 or 0). Memory of this type is *volatile*, meaning that its contents are lost when the power is turned off.

In the case of mainframe computers, core store memory was normally used. The memory devices in this case are tiny magnetic rings, threaded onto a matrix of criss-crossing wires. The direction of magnetization in a ring is determined by the current flowing through the wires, one direction representing a binary 0, the other a binary 1. Because the rings remain magnetized even when the power is turned off, the data is retained. So this type of memory is called *non-volatile*.

In both types of memory, the individual devices – transistors or rings – are laid out in rectangular arrays, each one occupying a location or *address* that can be identified by its row and column numbers. These numbers are, of course, in binary digital form. Each item of data stored in memory therefore has associated with it a *memory address*.

When the CPU reads an item of data from memory, it has to do two things:

1   Look up the address of the data in memory.
2   Read the data, i.e. the sequence of 0s and 1s, at that address.

The numbers identifying memory addresses travel in electronic form down an *address bus* inside the computer, those representing the data travel down a *data bus*.

## 2.25  Read only memory

Read only memory, or ROM, is a permanent store on microchip, normally used for holding programs. In this type of memory the tiny transistor switches cannot be turned ON or OFF, but are permanently encoded at the time of the chip's manufacture to produce the required program. These chips are called *read only* because it is not possible to write new programs or data to them.

The advantage of using ROM chips instead of storing data on disk and reading it into RAM as required is:

- It is more convenient to have frequently-used software immediately available inside the computer instead of on disk.
- When the computer is running, all of the RAM is left free for data (though note that for the PC the 640K limit applies to both ROM and RAM).

If the computer has a hard disk (see next chapter), the first of these is of little account, as the software can be almost as quickly loaded from the hard disk. However, ROM-based software is useful (sometimes essential) in the case of laptop and hand-held computers which lack a hard disk (or sometimes any sort of disk).

The disadvantages of ROM-based software are:

- The relatively high cost compared to disk storage.
- It may be difficult to upgrade to later versions of the software.

Some ROMs can be erased and reprogrammed. These are called EPROMS (short for Erasable Programmable ROM). You can recognize one of these by the small glass window in the surface of its casing, below which is the actual microchip (see Figure 1.1). The contents of the chip can be erased by exposing it to ultraviolet light for about 20 minutes, and it can then be reprogrammed by loading a new program into it.

## 2.26   The memory map

I've said that memory on the PC is limited to 640K. This is not strictly true – the CPU is able to access up to 1 Mb. However, the area of memory above 640K (the top 360K) is reserved for system tasks such as controlling the output to the monitor. The 640K is the amount of memory reserved for programs and data, including the operating system itself which takes up about 40K. (The exact amount depends on the version of the operating system.)

It is in fact possible to add many Mbytes of 'expanded' memory. The CPU is not able to access this directly, but what it can do is swap a 64K chunk of this memory into a 64K 'page frame' located in the top 360K of ordinary memory, and access that. By rapidly swapping different 64K pages of expanding memory in and out of this page frame area, it can in effect scan the entire memory.

For this to work, the expanded memory has to conform to the so-called LIM (Lotus-Intel-Microsoft) standard, and any software which wishes to use this facility has to be written to this standard. It sounds complicated, but it works well enough. In fact the software I am using to write this book, and the text itself, are residing in the expanded memory area of my computer, leaving virtually the entire 640K of ordinary memory free for other things. This means that I can run other software at the same time, should I so wish, and jump instantly between my writing work and other computing activities.

## 2.27   Types of computer

Computers can be classified in a variety of ways. Traditionally, they have been divided into *mainframe, mini*, and *microcomputers*, but with the increasing power of microcomputers this distinction is becoming blurred.

The largest type of computer is the *mainframe*, which takes its name from the big metal cabinet or 'frame' which was originally required to house the central processing unit. In the past, a mainframe might occupy a large room and cost millions of pounds (and be less powerful than modern PCs!). Even today it must be housed in a number of sizeable cabinets, and costs are of the order of £100,000 and upwards. A mainframe can cope with the data processing requirements of a large business, having the following advantages over smaller computers:

- It processes data at higher speeds, and so handles large jobs more quickly.
- The disk drives can store much more data than is possible in a smaller system, and they can therefore handle larger files.
- Its operating system allows a number of people to use it simultaneously, through a technique called *multiprogramming* (see page 207). They are connected to it by keyboard-and-screen units called *terminals* or *visual display units* (VDUs).

*Minicomputers* are cut-down mainframes, often costing between £10,000 and £20,000, and able to handle the work of smaller organizations. A mini will be smaller than a mainframe, its storage capacity will be smaller, and it will not be able to support so many users at the same time.

*Microcomputers* are the desktop machines that have swept the computer scene in the last decade. They include hand-held devices and home computers, as well as business machines. The latter are called *personal computers*, because they are intended for the use of a single individual rather than for shared use by a number of people.

Today, personal computers are often *networked*, meaning that they are connected by cable to each other and to central facilities such as large hard disks and printers. Networked PCs can, in many organizations, perform the type of task that required mainframe or minicomputers in the past. They can share large files of data, and, with the processing speeds of modern microprocessors, execute large data processing tasks at high speeds.

Personal computers are therefore taking over much of the computing work in many organizations, leaving mainframes and minis for specialist tasks requiring massive processing such as airline bookings systems, banking systems, and factory control. Even these areas may eventually be taken over by the next generation of RISC-based microcomputers that are now beginning to appear.

## 2.28   Computer generations

Another way of classifying computers is by generation.

- The *first generation* of computers were in operation in the 1950s, and their CPUs were built out of thermionic valves. As explained earlier, these computers were very large, expensive, and unreliable, and their performance was feeble by today's standards. (Today's computers are about a million times faster!) Also, they consumed a great deal of electricity and generated a lot of heat, so cooling systems had to be built in. Internal memory was by means of magnetic drums (similar in principle to today's magnetic disks), so memory access times were slow.
- The *second generation* were in operation in the early 1960s, the thermionic valves being replaced by transistors (which at that time had to be soldered together rather than incorporated into a chip). These were smaller, cheaper, and more reliable than valves, and they consumed less electricity and produced less heat. They were about a thousand times faster than first-generation computers. Internal memory was by means of core storage.
- The *third generation* came into existence in the mid 1960s, when microchips became available (consisting of many transistors and other components etched onto the surface of the chip). These were much smaller, cheaper, and faster than individual transistors soldered together. Processing times increased by a further factor of 1,000 at this time. Another characteristic of the third generation was the appearance of high-level programming languages such as COBOL and FORTRAN (see Chapter 4).
- *Fourth-generation computers* are characterized by chips exhibiting very large-scale integration (VLSI) of com-

ponents. VLSI chips were developed at the start of the 1970s, and are, in effect, computers on a chip. Fourth-generation computers are generally dated from the mid-1970s, and include the current generation of microcomputers. Various software innovations also characterize this generation, including systems network architecture and fourth-generation programming languages (see Chapter 4).

- The *fifth generation* is still largely on the drawing board, and is characterized by its ability to handle image recognition, speech recognition, and other artificial intelligence capabilities (see Chapter 5). Parallel processing techniques based on RISC chips (or their successors) will be a feature of these computers.

## 2.29 The evolution of the personal computer

Computers have been with us for less than half a century, yet they have transformed our world. The biggest change has taken place over the last 15 years, with the advent of fourth-generation computers, especially personal computers. There are now 40 million personal computers in use worldwide! Their impact has been so profound that it's worth devoting a few pages to their evolution.

The first microcomputers appeared in the mid 1970s. They included the legendary Apple I and Apple II computers, and the Commodore PET. These computers were little more than toys by today's standards, endowed with a mere 16K of memory or less, storage by means of cassette tape, and low-powered 8-bit processors. Nevertheless they were cheap (by the standards of the day), easy to use, and you could use them to write letters and, if you were an enthusiast, to program.

What brought these computers to the attention of the business community was the appearance of a program called Visicalc. This was the world's first spreadsheet, and it was written for the Apple. It turned out to be just the kind of thing that managers and decision makers needed (see Chapter 6), and so large numbers of them bought the Apple just to run Visicalc.

The giant IBM manufactured only large computers at this

time, and was reluctant to move into micros. One reason for this reluctance was the fact that micros on managers' desks threatened the power and the jobs of the people who actually purchased IBM's products, namely data processing personnel. Another was the destabilizing effect that such micros would have on IBM's large and profitable mainframe market.

However, by the start of the 1980s the highly successful Apple computer was making significant inroads into the business computing market, and IBM had to respond. In August 1981 it launched its first microcomputer, the original PC.

## 2.30　The IBM PC

Technologically, the PC was no great advance on the older Apple and PET microcomputers. There were problems with the keyboard, the screen resolution was not all that good, it had only 64K of memory, and the operating system (DOS) was simply a rehash of the older CP/M operating system. The reason for the PC's remarkable success was the badge on the front that said 'IBM'.

At that time IBM dominated the computer market to a much greater extent than it does today. It offered its customers a coherent range of products, with a natural upgrade route from less powerful to more powerful and from older to newer. It offered them maintenance and other support, and it offered them the security of dealing with a supplier who, without doubt, was not going to collapse and disappear. Apple Computing, however good its product, could offer none of these benefits – although, in retrospect, it has not disappeared and in the second half of the 1980s enjoyed a marked increase in popularity and profitability.

IBM's entry into the microcomputer market provided just the push that commerce and industry needed to embrace this most important component of the information technology revolution. Companies were prepared to buy the PC because the IBM badge gave it credibility. Software houses were prepared to write packages for it, because there was a large and growing market. More people were prepared to buy the PC because of this growing range of software, and this encouraged yet more software houses to enter the fray. An exponential growth set in, with ever more customers buying and ever more and better software being sold, to the benefit of all. The PC had set the industry standard for producers and users, and the microcomputer had come of age.

But this benign circle of users and software producers was not the only reason for the wholesale adoption of the PC. Another factor helped to fuel the boom, one which IBM had built into its computer without realizing where it would lead.

## 2.31 The clones and the add-ons

Whatever the defects of IBM's personal computer, it had two uniquely redeeming features that have greatly helped the IT revolution:

- It was an *open architecture* machine, meaning that it was designed to be expandable by adding on additional circuitry.
- Its design can easily be copied.

The large growing PC market encouraged other manufacturers to exploit these features, to the advantage of everyone (except possibly IBM).

- There are many companies offering a variety of *expansion cards*, i.e. circuit boards containing chips which can be fixed in the expansion slots inside the PC's casing. These cards offer a range of facilities and enhancements, including improved screen displays, speech recognition, greater processing power, and so on.
- There are now many companies making and assembling personal computers which are virtually identical to the IBM PC and its successors. These are called *PC-compatibles*, or *clones*. They are able to run the same software as the real thing, but are normally cheaper and often offer superior performance.

What is so extraordinary is that although these computers comprise by far the largest segment of the market, IBM itself no longer manufactures them!

## 2.32   The IBM AT

As was explained earlier, the IBM PC was based on the Intel 8086 chip. This was looking distinctly long in the tooth by the mid 1980s, and it made the PC look weak besides some of the newer micros that were appearing, especially the Apple Macintosh (see below).

In August 1984 IBM launched the PC-AT ('AT' stood for 'advanced technology' – some would claim that this was more of a marketing ploy than a statement of truth!) This was designed to be compatible with the PC (i.e. run the same software) but to overcome some of the earlier machine's defects. One obvious external difference was the improved keyboard. Internally it had a more advanced CPU, based on the Intel 80286 chip. This enabled it to:

- Run a lot faster.
- Access memory above the 640K limit (in theory).
- Run several programs simultaneously (called *multi-tasking*).
- Allow simultaneous use of the CPU and hard disk by several users (called *multiusing*).

In practice, however, the full potential of this machine has never been exploited, so that it has been used simply as a fast PC. The reason is that the enhancements to the operating system necessary for it to access more memory and to multitask have yet to materialize (though in recent months Windows version 3 has appeared which does enable this).

## 2.33   The Apple Macintosh

The original Apple microcomputer brought to birth personal computing in business. It was conquered by the IBM PC, but Apple fought back with the Macintosh, which appeared shortly before the IBM AT. The Mac was far ahead of its day in terms of both hardware and software. It was based upon a much more powerful processor, the 68000 chip, and it introduced a way of working with computers which is only now becoming standard on the IBM PC family.

This way of working was based upon Rank Xerox's original research work in the 1970s, and involved the use of the mouse to point to different parts of the screen and to pick options, the use of a graphical rather than character-based display, and the use of icons (pictorial representations of computing entities such as files). Also, some excellent applications packages appeared for the Mac, which made full use of its graphical environment. A particular software innovation was desktop publishing, made possible by the Mac environment and the appearance, in the mid 1980s, of the desktop laser printer (see Chapter 3).

By 1987/88 the Mac was so far ahead in terms of graphics and publishing applications of anything that was available in the IBM PC world that it even seemed possible that it might topple IBM and its followers from their pre-eminent position. In the event, this has never happened. The reasons include:

- Corporate inertia against moving from the accepted standard.
- High prices of the Mac, and Apple's policy of keeping out competing manufacturers who would bring prices down.
- The knowledge that the PC world was moving towards, and catching up with, the Mac world.

Today, the IBM PC world has effectively caught up with the Mac in terms of the power of the hardware and the user interface. In retrospect, we can see that the value of the Mac was to popularize Xerox's revolutionary computer working environment, so that it is now the standard across almost the entire range of serious personal computing. As at the start of 1980s, at the start of the 1990s Apple has proved to be the pace setter but not the victor.

## 2.34   The IBM PS/2

In 1987 IBM ceased production of PCs and ATs, and brought out in their place its new PS/2 range (short for

Personal System/2). These are based on the same Intel chips as the PC and AT, and able to run standard PC software. However, they incorporated the superior *MicroChannel Architecture* (see below), and the superior VGA screen display (see page 67). They also offered a Mac-like computing environment called 'Presentation Manager'. A further advantage for users with IBM mainframes is their ability to easily connect with these and so act as terminals.

IBM hoped that large numbers of corporate users would abandon the old PC/AT standard and flock to its new machine. In fact, this has yet to happen. PC/AT machines seem to go from strength to strength. They continue to outsell all others, they are steadily becoming more and more powerful, and they have adopted the VGA screen display standard. Besides this, the new Windows version 3 environment for the PC is virtually identical to Presentation Manager, and a huge amount of applications software is currently being written for it – far more than is being produced for Presentation Manager.

## 2.35    Portable computers

At the moment, the largest hardware growth area within personal computing is the personal computer. As in other areas, PC-compatibles dominate the portable scene, with offerings from most manufacturers.

Portable computers fall into four categories:

- Mains-only portables, which in effect are small desktop PCs which can be easily carried around but which can't be used 'on the move'. Typically, these boast most of the facilities of desktop PCs – including hard disks – but weigh about 15 lbs.
- 'Laptop' computers which also offer most of the facilities of desktop PCs but which include rechargeable batteries and so can be used on the move. These may weigh as much as mains-only portables, and the batteries may only run for about 3 hours between charges.
- 'Notebook' computers which are much lighter – they weigh 6 lb or less – but which may lack some of the facilities of desktop PCs, such as hard disks. Some

notebook computers, such as the Poquet and the range from Psion, are not PC-compatible, and they may have keyboards which are rather small and awkward to use, but they have features which nevertheless make them tempting buys for people who want to write letters etc. on the move, such as a low price, a long battery life, and a low weight.

- Hand-held ('palm-top') computers, such as the Psion Organiser and the Microwriter Agenda (see Figure 2.7). These are more like electronic Filofaxes than computers, enabling you to maintain diaries, address lists, etc. in a box which weighs about 1 lb and which is about the size of a Filofax. They may include simple word processing and record keeping, and the Agenda includes a cable which enables you to transfer your work to a PC. They are limited by their tiny screen displays, which typically show 20 characters across by four lines deep, and by the tiny keyboards. However, the Agenda includes special 'Microwriter' buttons which, once you learn the various combinations, enable you to achieve a reasonable typing speed.

Leaving palm-top computers aside (as they are too tiny and awkward for normal use), the advantages of portables over ordinary desktop machines are:

- They occupy much less space on the desk. I am writing this book on a portable computer at home, where I would have problems trying to fit a desktop computer on my desk.
- They can be easily carried around for use in other locations, or, in the case of notebook computers, for use on the move.

The first portables lacked many of the features that were standard on desktops, such as large hard disks and good displays, and they were very expensive and fairly heavy. The latest models have come down in price, they offer excellent displays including colour on some models, they are quite light, and they have all the power of their larger brethren. It is reckoned that in few years portable PCs will become the most popular type of computer.

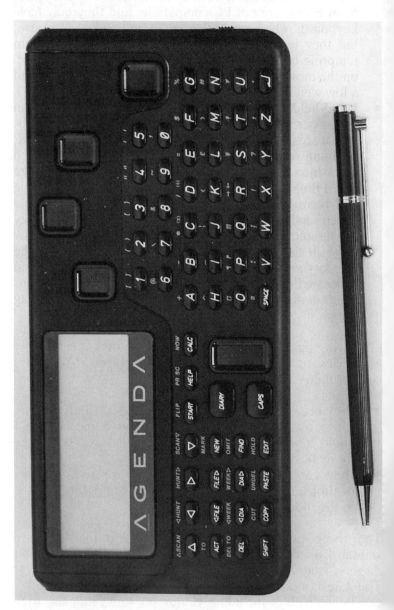

*Figure 2.7*   The Microwriter Agenda

## 2.36   Computer buses

The 'bus' in a computer is the wiring along which all the bits
that make up each item of the information travel in parallel.
An important feature of the IBM PC's bus is its expansion
capability – it provides a series of slots into which expansion
cards can be added (see page 47). The original PC bus
allowed only 8 bits to travel in parallel; when it introduced
the AT in 1984, IBM doubled the number of wires in the
bus so that it could handle 16 bits, and it also doubled its
speed to 8 MHz. The AT bus has proved very successful,
there are a large number of expansion cards available for it,
and it is still the standard in the PC world. It is now referred
to as the *Industry Standard Architecture* (ISA) bus.

One of the main features of the IBM PS/2 range of
computers which were introduced in 1987 was the radically
new *MicroChannel Architecture* (MCA) bus. This offered a
number of advantages over the AT bus:

- It doubled the number of wires to handle 32 bits.
- It could run much faster.
- It offered improved multitasking capabilities.
- It allowed expansion cards to use the bus without
  imposing additional work on the CPU.
- It allowed PS/2 computers to be directly linked to IBM
  mainframe and minicomputers and so act as terminals.

However, it was not compatible with the AT bus, which
meant that PS/2 computers lost an essential element of PC
compatibility, for they could not use any existing expansion
cards.

To compete with the superior technology of MCA, other
PC manufacturers led by Compaq announced (in 1988) that
a new *Extended Industry Standard Architecture* (EISA) bus
would be developed. Like MCA, this would be a 32-bit bus
and would run at a high speed, but it would be compatible
with the ISA bus and so take existing expansion cards. The
EISA bus is now available, and is provided as standard on
fast 80486 machines.

Being 32 bits, MCA and EISA buses are significantly

more expensive than the 16-bit ISA bus. At the present time they have little to offer most users, as few expansion cards are able to take advantage of the high speeds that they allow.

---

# 3
# Peripherals

## 3.1 Introduction

A *peripheral* is a device which is outside the central processing unit of a computer but controlled by it. There are four
main types of peripheral, namely input devices such as
keyboards, storage devices such as magnetic disks, output
devices such as monitors, and communication devices such
as modems.

The last chapter dealt with computers in general and
covered the work of the CPU. This chapter covers the
peripheral devices that might be connected to it. Modems
and other telecommunications devices will be covered later
in the chapter that deals with telecommunications (Chapter
8).

## 3.2 Input devices

A variety of input devices exist, able to convert information
in any form (data, text, speech, or image) into the binary
pulses recognized by computers. Some of these devices are
described below.

## 3.3 The keyboard

The keyboard is still the primary device for inputting
information to a computer, though it may ultimately be
superseded by voice input devices. It operates by converting
key presses to electronic signals in binary digital form.

The typical computer keyboard has the standard

'QWERTY' character keys inherited from the typewriter, together with a number of special keys described below. Alternative keyboard layouts have been designed, incorporating a more logical and natural arrangement of character keys, but these have never caught on.

The special keys vary somewhat according to the make of computer, but they usually include the following:

- *Function keys*, up to 12 in number, positioned either above or to the left of the character keys. These can be programmed by the user or by the software being run, so that a single key depression sends a command or string of commands to the computer.
- *The CTRL and ALT keys* (short for Control and Alternate), which are always used in conjunction with other keys to issue commands to the computer. For example, in the WordStar word processing software, CTRL and G, pressed at the same time, delete the character at the cursor position on the screen, CTRL and T delete the word at this position, and CTRL and Y delete the line.
- *The backspace key*, which deletes the character to the immediate left of the cursor on the screen.
- *The four 'arrow' keys*, which move the cursor one character position in the direction of the arrow (up, down, left, or right).
- *The PgUp and PgDn keys*, which are normally programmed by your word processing or other software to move the cursor one 'page' (i.e. screen) up or down.
- *The Home key*, which may be programmed to move the cursor to the left of the screen, or the beginning of the document.
- *The End key*, which may be programmed to move the cursor to the right of the screen, or the end of the document.
- *The Esc key*, which is often programmed to enable you to escape from your currently selected option or task.

## 3.4　The mouse

The *mouse* is a hand-held device with a rubber or metal ball protruding from its base (see Figure 3.1). As you push the

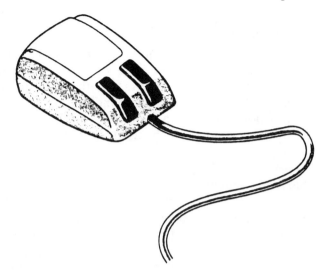

*Figure 3.1* A computer mouse

mouse over the surface of the desk, the movements of the ball are detected by the internal mechanism and converted to electrical signals. These are fed to the computer via a cable, and converted by the associated software to corresponding movements of the cursor across the screen. At the front of the mouse's casing are two or three buttons (or a single button in the case of the Macintosh mouse). You press these to perform tasks such as picking options displayed on the screen.

Similar to the mouse is the trackerball, used on some computers. In this, the casing remains stationary while the ball, which is at the top, is rolled with the fingers.

The mouse has proved very popular, and is now utilized by a great deal of software. In particular, it is much easier to use than the keyboard for the following operations:

- *Picking*, i.e. selecting options from a list displayed on the screen.
- *Pointing*, i.e. moving rapidly from one point to another in a word-processed document, file of records, or table of data.
- *Drawing*, i.e. constructing lines and other shapes on the screen.

On some computer systems, such as the Apple Macintosh, the Atari ST, the IBM PS/2, and PCs running Windows, the mouse is an essential part of the hardware, as the way in which you use the software on those systems is to a large extent based upon it (see Chapter 5). With other systems, such as PCs which do not use the Windows environment, the mouse is not essential, though some software running on those systems cannot easily be used without it.

### 3.5   Character-recognition devices

One type of character-recognition device enables the user to input text and numerical data by handwriting it in capital letters on a pressure-sensitive surface using a special pen. An invisible grid of the fine wires below the surface detects the shape of the letters, converting them to electrical signals which the computer interprets using special software. Although this device is a genuine replacement for the keyboard, it has never really caught on, being overtaken by other developments, in particular the advances being made in speech recognition devices described later.

Much more useful are the optical character readers (OCRs) which scan text which has been typed or printed on paper converting the characters to the binary code that the computer understands. These provide a way of passing information between machines which cannot communicate electronically. For example, they enable output from a typewriter to be passed to a word processor for editing and final printing, a technique that has been used in some typing pools. They also enable a business to convert its input documents to electronic form without the need to key them in.

Some modern image scanners, described later in this chapter, can also function as OCRs when used with special OCR software. These can recognize a reasonable range of typefaces, so enabling printed and typed text to be input to a computer. However, smeared characters and unusual typefaces may be beyond them. In place of a character that they can't recognize, they will substitute a special symbol. These symbols can be automatically picked out and replaced later on by spell-checking software.

## 3.6   The microphone

It is quite easy to convert the spoken word to a digital signal for computer input. The microphone converts audio signals to electrical waves, and these can be converted by electronic circuitry in the computer to digital form. What is difficult is the recognition, by the computer, of the signal, so that it can handle it in the same way as if it had been typed. Highly sophisticated speech-recognition software is required, able to match the sound uttered by the user with a vocabulary of sound signals stored in the computer, and to display the words on the screen as though they had been entered at the keyboard.

The development of viable speech-recognition systems for the English language has been a major goal of many researchers for a number of years. Recently, commercial systems have started to emerge. One major problem is the many inconsistencies between the written and spoken word in English. Japanese, in contrast, is phonetically very precise, and so speech-recognition systems for that language were relatively easy to develop and have been used for some time. English language systems face the task of having to infer, from the context, what the words are likely to be.

A second problem is the fact that there can be wide variations between the speech patterns of one individual and another. To cope with this, the system has to be 'trained' to recognize the user's particular speech. Most systems require him to read a passage containing all the words stored in the computer's vocabulary on disk, so that it is able to match what's spoken with what's stored. In this way it constructs speech 'templates' for the user, which it stores for use in all subsequent dictation sessions.

Speech-recognition systems in the past have suffered from either having too limited a vocabulary to be of much use, or else, in the case of large vocabulary systems, taking far too long to match what was spoken with what was stored in the computer. Recent increases in computer power have greatly speeded things up, and voice systems on personal computers have now appeared. The system from Apricot is called 'Dictate', and it has a vocabulary of 30,000 words. IBM has also developed a system for PCs. At the heart of the IBM system is a digital signal processor (DSP) which uses parallel processing techniques and is able to perform 10 million instructions per second.

The system works by recognizing the 200 or more phonetic elements of words, rather than by attempting to recognize a vast vocabulary of whole words. This means that the computer has to produce only a relatively small number of speech templates, and so the initial training session can be quite brief. To match the spoken word with what's stored in its vocabulary, the computer uses a statistical approach based on an analysis by the IBM researchers of some 25 million words of office correspondence. This approach enables it to predict what words are likely to appear together, and so to select likely candidates from its vocabulary.

When the first word is spoken, the computer makes a tentative assessment but does not display the candidate word on the screen. When the next word is spoken, the initial candidate is reassessed and either accepted or rejected in favour of another, and the result displayed. The process continues through the dictation session.

### 3.7    Video cameras and scanners

Video cameras are versatile devices, being able to capture images of any type, including solid objects. Scanners are limited to images on paper, but they are able to scan each spot on the paper with much greater accuracy than cameras, and so are more widely used for this type of input. Scanners provide a low-cost way of inputting material that's been typed or printed on paper into a computer system. (I say 'low cost' because rekeying an A4 page costs between £4 and £5.) More was said on this earlier in this chapter on page 58.

Most scanners incorporate a special sort of camera made up of *charged-coupled devices* (CCDs). Each CCD receives light from the image, and, provided the light is strong enough, will generate an electrical charge. This means that light areas or 'dots' of the image are represented by charged cells, and dark areas by uncharged cells. As the paper containing the image moves past the camera during the scanning process, these charges create electrical impulses which are fed into the computer, where they are interpreted by the scanning software as parts of the image.

The resolution of the typical scanner is 300 dots per inch, which means that it splits each square inch of the image up into a matrix of 300 × 300 tiny areas. This is better than the resolution of most computer screens, and the same as the resolution of most laser printers (see later in this chapter). Scanners typically cost between £1,000 and £2,000.

The technology behind this is well understood and quite straightforward. Nowadays, scanners are widely used to get drawings, diagrams, and photographs into computer systems for incorporation into documents and books which are made up electronically prior to printing. Much more difficult is the recognition of the image by the computer, so that it is able to act upon what it 'sees'. Just as the speech-recognition system described in the previous section worked by breaking down the spoken word into its phonetic elements, so image-recognition systems work by breaking down the image into component parts, identifying each and analysing their position relative to each other.

Image-recognition systems have been used for some years in industrial robots, but these devices have a limited 'vocabulary' of components, and the recognition process is highly complex and so relatively slow. It seems likely that the application of the transputer and parallel processing techniques will revolutionize image processing and image recognition in the future. This may lead not only to a new generation of industrial robots but also to new computer systems and applications which are able to perform tasks such as converting hand-drawn sketches into neat designs, and recognizing faces in a crowd.

## 3.8 Other input devices

Other input devices include:

- *Kimball tags*, used for stock control in some clothing stores. Attached to each article of clothing is one of these tags, recording data on the article as a pattern of punched holes. When the article is sold, the tag is removed and the data scanned into the store's computer.

- *Bar codes*, used for stock control in food stores. Here, the data is stored as a pattern of thin and thick lines printed on the product's packaging; the thin lines represent binary 0s, the thick lines 1s. At the checkout a light pen or similar device shines light across the pattern, the reflected light being translated into electrical pulses for computer input.
- *Magnetic ink character readers* (MICRs), used in banking. Cheques are identified by numbers printed with special magnetic ink, which can be read by an MICR and converted to binary digital form for computer input.

### 3.9   Storage devices

Because computer memory can hold only a limited amount of data and programs, and because, in the case of semiconductor RAM, it loses that data when the power is turned off, some form of long-term mass storage is essential. At the present time, magnetic disk is the main mass storage medium, though other types of mass storage are also used, in particular the optical disc described later.

Like the ordinary audio disc, a magnetic disk stores information on circular tracks marked out on its surface. As the disk rotates, an arm moves a read/write head to the required track, and 'reads' (i.e. retrieves) data from or 'writes' (i.e. stores) data to the spots on the track as they pass below it. The data is stored in digital form, a magnetized spot on the rotating surface representing a 1, a demagnetized spot a zero. As with an audio-cassette, information can be erased and re-recorded any number of times.

Magnetic tape can also be used in certain computer applications, but it is less versatile than disk, since it is not possible to move instantly to a particular spot on the tape to read or write data at that spot. Reading from the tape is rather like reading a novel: you must start at the beginning and read each word in sequence until you reach the end. This is called *sequential access*.

Reading from a disk is more like reading from a reference book: you look up the location of the section you require in an index and turn straight to the appropriate page. This is called *random access*. Each program or file of data on the disk must be assigned a name, and an index of these names is stored at the beginning of the disk. The location of the file on the disk's surface is also stored in an index, and when the computer receives a command to load a file into RAM it is able to read this location from the index and move the read/ write head directly to the required track on the disk's surface.

### 3.10 Floppy disks

There are two types of magnetic disk: *hard* disks (also called Winchester disks), and the smaller *floppy* disks (also called diskettes). Figure 3.2 shows the standard 5.25-inch diameter floppy disk, and as you can see it is enclosed in a protective flexible casing with an opening cut out to give the read/write head access to the magnetic surface. This type of disk is extremely light, and the disk-drive is able to bring it up to the required speed of rotation almost instantly. The disk-drive's motor only needs to be switched on by the computer when files are actually being accessed; the rest of the time the disk remains stationary in the drive.

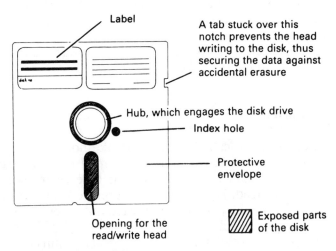

*Fig 3.2*   5.25-inch floppy disk

A disk must be *formatted*, i.e. magnetically configured to run on the particular computer system, before it can be used. This process marks out sectors on the surface within which the data is stored. In the case of PCs of the IBM-compatible variety, each track on the disk is divided into nine sectors, and each sector is able to store 512 bytes of data. There are 40 tracks on each side of a standard (low-density) floppy disk, giving $40 \times 512 = 184,320$ bytes for one side of the disk, i.e. 180K.

In the past, cheaper disk-drives had only one read/write head, and so were able to access only one side of the disk. Modern drives are able to access both sides of the disk, so 360K can be stored on a standard 5.25 inch floppy formatted for PCs. High-density drives on PCs allow you to store 1.2 Mbytes on two sides of a disk, though the more expensive high-density disk must be used in this case.

The smaller 3.5 inch disks are now becoming standard on personal computers (they have been used for many years on pace-setting computers such as the Apple Macintosh and the Atari ST). These disks are enclosed in a rigid plastic casing, and for added protection the read/write opening in the case is enclosed by a metal slider when the disk is removed from the drive. Despite their smaller size, these disks can store much more data than their larger 5.25 inch brethren, namely 720K in the case of double-sided standard density (i.e. low density) disks, and 1.44 Mbytes for high-density disks. 3.5 inch disks with capacities of 5 Mbytes or more are becoming available, and no doubt these will become the standard in the future.

## 3.11   Hard disks

Hard disks are so-called because, unlike floppies, they are of a sturdy, rigid construction. They are also much heavier than a floppy, and a hard disk-drive can take several seconds to get up to speed. Hard disks are therefore kept constantly spinning (while the computer is turned on), even when data is not being accessed.

The speed of rotation is very high, 3600 rev/min compared to 360 rev/min for floppy disks. At this speed, the movement of the air molecules adjacent to the disk's surface lifts the read/write head sufficiently to prevent it touching the surface. It can still access the data, but it does not cause any wear on the disk. The disk and the read/write head are enclosed in an airtight casing to prevent dust particles adhering to the disk's surface and interfering with the read/write process.

Hard disks have two advantages over floppies:

- They can store much more data – typical hard disks for microcomputers have capacities of 40, 80, or 120 Mbytes.
- They can access data 10 times faster than is possible with floppy disks.

Most personal computers nowadays have hard disks inside their casing. This saves fiddling with floppy disks whenever you want to load a program or load or save a file of data or text, and it greatly speeds up the loading of programs and data. Besides this, very large files, which may be too big to be held on a single floppy, will fit without difficulty onto the hard disk.

### 3.12  Optical (compact) discs

Compact discs are the same size as standard 5.25 magnetic disks, but use laser light technology to store data. Because a laser light beam can be focused with a high degree of precision, the tracks on these discs can be much closer together than is the case with magnetic disks. As a result they have very high capacities, measured in hundreds of Mbytes (typically, 600 Mbytes). The same technology used for recording and playing music CDs is used in computer compact discs. Another advantage is the fact that data is more secure on compact discs, as it can't be corrupted by magnetic fields.

Data is encoded on an optical disc by burning tiny pits in its surface with laser light. A pit represents a binary 1, the absence of a pit represents 0. Laser light is also used to read data from the disc, the pits and non-pits setting up different light-interference patterns that can be detected by the reading head. Retrieval times are faster than floppy drives, though not as fast as hard disk systems.

Several types of compact disc systems are available for computers. These are:

- *CD-ROM.* Like music CDs, these are 'pressed' by the manufacturer with whatever data he wishes to supply. Large databases of information can be supplied in this way, as can software.
- *CD-WO.* This is the *WORM* drive ('Write Once, Read Many Times'), which the user can write to, but can't erase. WORM drives are an excellent medium for archiving data.
- *CD-I.* This is interactive CD, under development by Philips for multimedia applications. This is described on page 169.
- *Erasable optical discs.* These use magneto-optical (MO) technology, and like ordinary magnetic disks allow you to record and erase data as often as you like. Unlike ordinary optical discs, the active layer of these discs is magnetized. To write a binary 1 to a spot on this layer, a pulse of laser light is focused on it, heating it up to several hundred degrees. At this temperature its magnetic polarity can be altered by a magnet which is activated on the opposite side of the disc. (The remaining cold spots will be unaffected by this magnet.) Erasable optical drives are currently very expensive, but prices will no doubt fall in the future.

### 3.13 Output devices – monitors

The main output devices are monitors and printers. We'll deal with monitors in this section, and printers in the next.

The resolution (or clarity) of the picture that monitors achieve is determined by the number of *pixels*, or 'picture elements', on the screen. High resolution monitors have resolutions of 2000 by 2000 pixels, though few present-day computers are able to provide images which take advantage of this degree of clarity. The old-fashioned IBM PC, for example, with a Colour Graphics Adaptor (CGA), can only output images with a resolution of 640 pixels horizontally by 200 vertically. This was adequate for character-based displays, but for graphics it was hopelessly inferior to the displays of more advanced machines such as the Apple Macintosh.

In the mid-1980s IBM introduced the Enhanced Graphics

Adaptor (EGA), which offered a higher resolution. This gave a much better clarity, though it was still not as good as the Mac. Then, in the 1987, IBM brought out the Video Graphics Array (VGA) on its PS/2 range of microcomputers, with a resolution of 640 by 480. This was quickly taken up by the PC-compatible world, and is now the standard. In 1990 IBM brought out its Extended Graphics Array (XGA), with a resolution of 1024 by 768 pixels and support for 65,000 colours, and 'Super VGA' with the same resolution also became available from competing manufacturers, so perhaps these will become the standards in the future.

### 3.14 Cathode ray tubes

Most computer monitors are based on cathode ray tubes (CRTs), similar to those used in TV sets. They consist of one or more 'guns' which fire streams of electrons at a special chemical which backs the surface of the monitor. These electron streams repeatedly scan the screen from top to bottom, dot by dot and line by line, each scan taking only a fraction of a second. In colour screens, there are three guns, one for each of the colours red, green and blue. These cause each dot on the screen to generate red, green, or blue light, the combination of these three giving the full colour spectrum. CRTs give a bright picture, with good colours, but they are bulky and consume a relatively large amount of power.

Monochrome models display text and graphics as either green on a black background, orange on a black background, or white on a black background. (The foreground and background colours can be reversed by software.) Monochrome monitors are quite cheap, and they give a sharp picture. They are well suited for office applications, such as word processing, which do not require colour.

The more expensive colour or *RGB* monitors give colour displays, but the picture sharpness on the cheaper models will not be as good as that achieved by monochrome monitors. RGB stands for Red-Green-Blue, and the CRTs in these monitors contain the three electron guns described above, each directly controlled by the computer.

### 3.15   Flat screens

Portable computers require screens which are light, occupy little space, and, in the case of battery-operated models, don't consume much power. The various types of flat screen that are on the market meet this need. Unlike CRTs, though, the brightness of the image is generally limited, and, at the time of writing, very few flat screen monitors give colour displays.

*Liquid crystal display* (LCD) monitors are used on battery-operated portable computers, as these consume very little power. (This is the type of display used on digital watches.) However, compared to CRTs the displays tend to lack contrast and in some light conditions are not very legible, though the newer 'supertwist' LCD displays are quite good.

In an LCD, the image is formed by so-called liquid crystals. These are long rod-like molecules which, though solid, can flow like a liquid. Each pixel on the screen consists of a microscopic electrode positioned below several of these molecules. As the output from the computer scans the screen a row at a time, it activates each of these pixels in turn, switching it on or off. When a pixel is 'on', the crystals twist in such a way that they block out the light. When it is 'off', they let the light through. In early LCDs, the crystals were not very 'liquid', i.e. they did not respond very rapidly to the signal, but modern types of liquid crystal are much faster.

Colour LCDs require very fast liquid crystals. In what's called *passive matrix* systems there are three screens, coloured red, green, and blue, which are placed on top of each other. Below the three screens are the thousands of pixel electrodes which generate the light. The pixels in each screen act as filters for this light. If a pixel is to be red, for example, the green and blue filters above it are turned on, blocking out those colours, but the red filter is off, allowing the red light through. By turning the filters on and off in other combinations, other colours can be obtained.

Passive matrix displays are not very bright, however, since to display red, for example, light from only one out of the three crystals is allowed through the filters. They also consume too much power to be viable for battery-powered computers, and the screen refresh rate is rather slow. So *active matrix* displays are being developed, which use thin film transistor (TFT) screens. In these, there is a single screen, each pixel of which has three sub-pixels coloured red, green, and blue. These sub-pixels are separately activated to produce the colour output. Active matrix screens are, at the present time, difficult to manufacture and very expensive, so they are available on only a few top-of-the-range portables.

Two other types of flat screen are sometimes used for computer monitors, namely the *gas plasma* display, and the *electroluminescent* display. These are both light-emitting displays, and give a very clear, legible output, but they consume almost as much power as a conventional monitor. They are therefore suitable for portable computers which are designed to run off the mains, but not for battery-powered models. These displays are monochrome only – typically orange on a black or brown background, as this is reckoned to be both highly legible and restful on the eyes.

### 3.16   Output devices – printers

Computer printers are used to produce *hard-copy* of computer output, normally data or text, but also, in the case of certain printers, graphics (i.e. image, such as drawings or charts). Printers vary in their capabilities so far as text enhancements (such as underlining or emboldening) are concerned, and also in their ability to print graphics.

Most printers are designed to receive data 'in parallel' from the computer, 8 bits at a time. These have to be connected to the parallel port (socket) on the computer, also called the *Centronics* port, and sometimes labelled LPTI (short for Line Printer 1). The connecting cable will contain a number of parallel wires, and may take the form of a *ribbon cable*, so-called because it is flat and wide, like a ribbon.

Some printers are designed to receive data 'in serial' from the computer, i.e. one bit at a time. These have to be connected to the serial port (socket) on the computer, also called the RS-232 port, and sometimes labelled COM1 (short for Communications 1). This is the port used by the computer to communicate with other computers, and I will say more about this in Chapter 8.

Computer printers also differ in other respects:

- There are character printers (which print one character at a time), line printers (which print a line at a time), and page printers (which print a page at a time).
- A variety of printing technologies are possible, the main ones being dot matrix, daisy wheel, and laser.
- Some printers can handle only text, whereas others can handle text and graphics.
- There are a variety of standards for *control codes*, which are commands sent from the computer to the printer to turn on effects such as underlining and emboldening.

However, most software packages are able to cope with these differences. They do so by means of *printer drivers*, special programs which adapt the output from the software to the printer. All you have to do is to select your printer's name from the list that is presented to you when you first use the software.

The main types of printer are described below. The main differences between them are:

- Their quality of output.
- Whether they are able to print graphics.
- Their print speed.
- Their purchase price.

### 3.17   Dot matrix printers

These are inexpensive, relatively fast, and versatile, and therefore very popular. The print mechanism consists of a matrix of tiny needles. By hitting selected needles so that they stand out from the rest, the printer is able to create the shape of a letter or other character, which is then transferred to the paper via an inked ribbon. The print speed is typically 100 characters per second or more, and these printers are able to produce double size or very small characters, or bold print, italics, or other effects. They are also able to print pictures or graphs, if used with graphics software.

However, the print quality is not all that high, since the characters are not perfectly formed but consist of a pattern of dots. The resolution of most dot matrix printers is around 100 to 150 dots per inch. To overcome this defect, many dot matrix printers offer a *near-letter quality* (NLQ) mode. When in this mode, the print head prints each line twice, the second pass slightly offset from the first, which has the effect of filling in the gaps between the holes and making the characters more perfectly formed. This gives results which, although not of the highest quality, are acceptable for most correspondence.

One of the earliest and most popular dot matrix printers for personal computers is the Epson FX-80. This has set a standard for control codes (for emboldening, graphics, etc.) which many other manufacturers of dot matrix printers have followed. Almost all software supports this standard, and nowadays you can buy an Epson-compatible for as little as £150.

A related type of printer is the *line printer*, used in the data processing departments of large organizations for high-volume work. This is a much faster machine, and much more expensive. One version has up to 160 print wheels arranged in the form of a barrel, with characters embossed on each wheel, and able therefore to print up to 160 characters (a complete line) simultaneously. The quality is similar to that of the dot matrix printer, but no NLQ mode is provided.

## 3.18 Ink-jet printers

Like dot matrix printers, these create the shape of characters from a pattern of dots on the paper, but in this case the dots are created by squirting particles of ink from a fine jet. The quality is higher than that of dot matrix printers, almost as good as laser printers (see below), and being non-impact they are much quieter. Colour ink-jets are also available.

Ink-jets have recently come down in price, and they now compete directly with better quality dot matrix models. They are therefore likely to increase their share of the market in the future.

### 3.19   Daisy wheel printers

The print head in this type of printer is a *daisy wheel*, a circular device with a diameter of 3 inches which resembles a daisy flower. The print characters are embossed on the tip of each 'stalk'. When printing, the wheel rotates to bring the required character uppermost, and a hammer strikes it against an ink or carbon ribbon and so produces the printed impression on the paper. The print quality is high, much better than that of dot matrix printers, and slightly superior to that of the current generation of desktop laser printers.

The cheaper daisy wheel printers cost about the same as the Epson FX-80 or equivalent dot matrix printers, but they are much slower, generally printing at 13 to 15 characters per second. A fast daisy wheel printer – that is, one printing at 40 or 50 characters per second – will cost several times this amount.

Because the print head is made up of preformed embossed characters, this type of printer is not as versatile as the dot matrix variety. It cannot print graphics, and if you wish to change the type style from e.g. normal to italics, you have to change daisy wheels.

### 3.20   Laser printers

Laser-beam printers, commonly called laser printers, are page printers, meaning that they print an entire page at a time. In fact, they resemble photocopiers in size and appearance (see Figure 3.3), and employ a similar technology. They are very fast, typical speeds being around 8 pages per minute, and virtually silent in operation. The print quality is good, almost equal to that of daisy wheel printers. The resolution of current models is 300 dots per inch (dpi), though some of the latest versions offer 600 dpi. Most laser printers can handle graphics as well as text.

They therefore offer the quality of the daisy wheel with the versatility of the dot matrix, while being faster and quieter than either. Their print quality is higher than that of ink-jet printers, but they are more expensive.

The print mechanism in a laser printer consists of a laser light, rollers, and ink, and works as follows. A sheet of

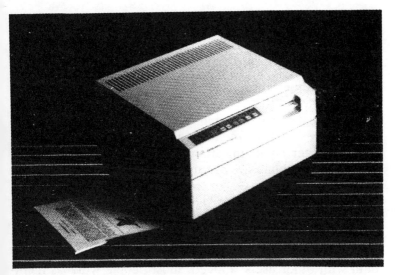

*Figure 3.3*  The Centronics PP-8 laser printer

paper is fed from a tray into the machine, and receives an electrostatic charge across its surface. The laser beam then rapidly and invisibly traces the computer's output (text or graphics) as a pattern of tiny dots on the paper, a process which removes the electrostatic charge from the points where the beam strikes the paper. The paper then receives a fine spray of ink across its surface, which adheres to the points with no charge but which is washed off the rest. After passing between rollers, the paper emerges, heated and dried, at the front of the machine.

## 3.21  Plotters

A plotter is an output device for producing hard-copy of a drawing or design done on a computer. It consists of a flat surface on which a piece of paper can be fixed, together with a moving arm to which a pen is attached. The pen reproduces on the paper the design that has been built up on the computer screen. By automatically replacing the pen by another from a bank of pens at the side of the surface the plotter is able to produce multicoloured diagrams.

The price varies from a few hundred to several thousand

pounds, the more expensive plotters permitting larger sheets of paper and working at higher speeds.

## 3.22　Communications devices and connectivity

For long-distance data communications over the telephone line, devices such as *modems* and *fax machines* are used. For computer communications within a building, network devices and cabling are required. All these are covered in Chapter 8.

*Connectivity* is the term applied to computer communications and networking. In many offices today PCs are networked, giving the user the advantage of having a 'personal' computer while at the same time sharing files and data with other users. Indeed, most people work as members of a group rather than in isolation, and connected computers are therefore better able to meet the needs of the work situation. Some software, such as Lotus' Notes, is designed for work groups using networked computers.

We can list the advantages of having networked rather than stand-alone (i.e. unconnected) PCs as follows:

- Resources, such as hard disks and printers, can be shared.
- Software can be stored on a shared hard disk instead of being duplicated on every individual computer's disks.
- Files of data, stored on a shared hard disk, can be accessed by everyone.
- Electronic mail (i.e. memos and other messages that are typed on the screen but not printed, 'email' for short) can be passed from one machine to another, providing a fast and low-cost messaging system.
- Incompatible hardware, such as PCs and Macs, can be linked by means of the network and files passed between them.
- Data is less likely to be accidentally erased and lost, as formal housekeeping procedures will normally be instituted, under the control of the network manager, for carrying out tasks such as making regular backups.

So besides allowing office staff to share resources and services, networking means that they can also share databases, diaries, and other sources of information, and electronic mail (messages) can be passed between them.

In a network there must be a 'host' computer. This is the *file server*, so called because it holds, on its hard disk, the files used by the other computers on the network. (The file server may be able to also act as an ordinary networked computer or workstation, though the person using it may find that some operations are slowed down as part of its processing resources are servicing the network.) The other computers connected to the network may be called *clients, terminals*, or *stations*.

So far as personal computers are concerned, the most common type of network is the *local area network*, or LAN. In this, the various computers and other equipment are linked together by a single long coaxial cable laid around the site. Besides this cabling, each must normally have a network card containing special network circuitry installed inside its casing. For more detail on networking, see page 178.

# 4
# Languages and programs

## 4.1 The importance of software

So far, we've looked at computer hardware. With this chapter we turn to software, i.e. the programs of instructions that tell the computer what to do. In fact, much of the rest of this book is about software. That's because software is the most important part of a computer system. The hardware is useful only insofar as it enables the software to operate.

Computers are becoming more and more alike, especially in the world of business microcomputing. Like motor cars, they come in differently shaped boxes, and the contents of those boxes may differ slightly. But so far as you, the user, are concerned, they all behave in much the same way. They handle screens, disk-drives, and printers in what seems the same way, and most will run the same or similar software.

If a fantastic new software product comes out on the Apple Macintosh, within a couple of years it will also be available on IBM-PCs and compatibles, the Atari ST, and others. Likewise successful products running on the PC are soon available on the Apple Mac. If you want to use the Lotus 1-2-3 spreadsheet package, or Microsoft's Excel, or the WordPerfect word processor, or Microsoft's Word, to name but a few, then you can buy any of the machines I've mentioned. For most computer tasks, it makes little difference which hardware you buy – it's the software that counts.

And whatever the hardware merits of the Macintosh, the Atari ST, or the Commodore Amiga, they do not run as much software as the PC. Which is one reason why some 40 million PCs have been sold world-wide, compared to a fraction of that number for other makes. So newer micros, such as the Acorn Archimedes, provide PC emulators – software or hardware add-ons that make the machine behave just like a PC, able to run the PC's software. Some micros, such as the Atari and the Amiga, enable you to emulate several other machines. These emulators slow down the running speed considerably, but computers like the Archimedes are so fast that the performance is still acceptable. In fact, we cannot be many years away from the day when a single box will be able to emulate almost anything, and therefore to run almost any software that you care to buy.

## 4.2 What is software?

So what is computer software? It consists of sets of computer instructions, stored on magnetic disk, semiconductor ROM, or other suitable storage device. To run these instructions, the computer loads them from the storage device into RAM, and they are then executed by the CPU. In the case of computers based upon conventional microprocessors, the instructions are executed serially, i.e. one after another. In the case of computers based upon the transputer, many of the instructions are executed in parallel, i.e. at the same time.

The computer needs software to tell it how to carry out its various tasks:

- It needs *system software* to carry out 'system' tasks like formatting disks, reading files on the disk, controlling the screen display, and so on.
- It needs *application software* to carry out its various applications, such as writing letters, keeping records, and producing drawings or charts.

I shall be describing both of these types of software in subsequent chapters. In this chapter I shall deal mainly with how software is written. The process of writing software is known as *coding*, and the resulting code is known as a *program*.

## 4.3   How software works

An instruction contained in a computer program takes the form of a sequence of bits (binary 0s and 1s). When the instruction is executed, these bits travel as electrical pulses to the CPU. Here, logic gates contained in special control circuits make these bits close switches in a second circuit along which the computer data flows. In this way the program operates on data.

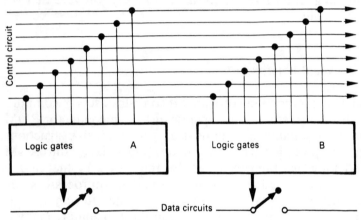

*Figure 4.1*   A control circuit in a computer

This is represented diagrammatically in Figure 4.1. Each type of action that the computer can perform – such as addition, subtraction, or a logical operation – has associated with it a particular set of logic gates. The bits flowing down the control circuit pass each set of logic gates, but only one set will output a current and so close a switch.

## 4.4   Programming languages

In the early days of computing, programmers wrote these instructions as sequences of binary 0s and 1s. This is called *machine code*, as it is the code or 'language' that the machine understands. A program to carry out quite a simple task will consist of many machine code instructions, and so program-writing in the early days was a time-consuming and arduous task. Machine code is sometimes called the 'first generation' programming language.

To simplify matters and speed up the task of programming, *assembly languages* were developed. These were one stage removed from machine code in the direction of human-understandibility, and are sometimes called 'second generation' programming languages. With these, programmers could write instructions in an easier form, using commands such as LDA, meaning 'load accumulator', ADC, meaning 'add with carry', and CLC, meaning 'clear carry'. The assembly language converts these commands into the strings of binary 0s and 1s that the computer understands.

Although these commands take away the need to know anything about the sequence of bits that must be sent to the control circuit, they do demand a good knowledge of what goes on inside the computer in order to perform even simple tasks such as addition or subtraction. For example, you need to know that numbers to be added or subtracted have to be loaded into the accumulator (a special area of working memory in the CPU), and you have to tell the computer to 'carry' numbers when performing addition. Here is the sequence of assembly language commands for adding 2 and 2 on computers which use the 6502 microprocessor (such as the original Apple computer or the BBC micro). An explanation is given at the right of each command.

| | |
|---|---|
| LDA #&2 | Put the number 2 into the accumulator |
| CLC | Clear carry before addition |
| ADC #&2 | Add 2 to the contents of the accumulator |
| STA &70 | Store the result in memory location &70 |

Because in both machine code and assembly language you are working close to the level of the computer and require an intimate knowledge of the way in which it works, they are called *low-level languages*. Furthermore, since these languages are addressing the actual circuitry inside the CPU, they are machine-dependent, meaning that they vary from one type of computer to another. So computers based on the 6502 microprocessor use a different assembly language to PCs which are based on the Intel 8086 family of microprocessors.

Nowadays, most programming is done in *high-level languages*. They are called this because they are a further level away from the level of the machine, and their commands are such that you don't need to know anything about the computer's circuitry in order to write programs. The commands are, in fact, fairly close to the language of ordinary English and arithmetic. For example, to add two variables A and B in many high-level languages, you simply type 'A + B'.

This not only makes programming easier, it means that programs written in these languages are not restricted to particular types of microprocessor. In theory, such a program will run on any computer, though some modifications may be required to cope with hardware differences, e.g. screen display differences. In practice, some languages, notably BASIC, vary somewhat from computer to computer, and BASIC programs written for one may require extensive modifications before they will run on another.

Although programs in high-level languages are relatively easy for humans to write, they are not directly comprehensible to the computer, which needs detailed instructions in the form of binary 0s and 1s. So the computer must translate these commands into its low-level language. The high-level language program written by the programmer is called the *source program*, the machine-language translation is called the *object program*.

With some high-level languages, this translation job takes place while the program is being run. This means that the computer has to translate commands and execute them at the same time, which slows the program down. This type of translation is called *interpretation* and is carried out by a piece of system software called an *interpreter*. The most well-known interpreted language is BASIC (see page 83). Interpreted languages require relatively small amounts of computer memory to run, one reason why BASIC became so popular on microcomputers, which used to have severely limited amounts of RAM.

With most high-level languages, however, the program is translated *before* it is run. This type of translation is called *compilation*, and is carried out by a piece of software called a *compiler*. A program that has been translated is said to be *compiled*. It is then run in its compiled form. Compiled programs don't need the presence of the original language in the computer in order to run, and they run much faster than programs that have to be interpreted. Because of these advantages, compiled versions of BASIC have been produced and are available on many computers.

Well-known compiled languages are COBOL and C, both of which are standardized across a wide range of machines. COBOL is mainly used on large computers, and is the language of data processing, and C is used across a range of computers including microcomputers. A program written in C can be compiled for a variety of different computers, and then sold in its compiled form for those computers.

Many hundreds of programming languages exist, each with their strengths and weaknesses. Three of the most widely used are FORTRAN, BASIC and COBOL, and these are described briefly below. I have also included a brief account of PROLOG, which is a quite different type of language used mainly in expert system applications. These high-level languages are sometimes called 'third generation' programming languages.

## 4.5 FORTRAN

The development of FORTRAN was started by IBM in 1954, and it was first put to use in that organization in 1957. FORTRAN is short for FORmula TRANslation and, as this name implies, it was designed for engineering, statistics, and other mathematically-oriented applications. It is good at carrying out complex calculations, which can be coded as compressed statements much like ordinary mathematical formulae. It requires a large compiler, which limited its use to computers with reasonably large amounts of memory.

Being almost the first high-level language, FORTRAN became firmly entrenched as the language for scientific use, and it still retains that position. BASIC, the most popular language of all for general-purpose use, was derived from FORTRAN.

A program written in FORTRAN consists of a list of numbered statements, called program lines, which express in a compact form a sequence of instructions to the computer. There are four kinds of statement, which we can think of as analogous to the four kinds of task – control, arithmetic/logic, input and output – that go on in a computer system (see the start of Chapter 2):

- Control statements.
- Arithmetic statements.
- Input statements.
- Output statements.

Control statements tell the computer how to sequence its execution of the program. Normally, the program lines will be executed in numbered order, but if in line 50 there is the control statement GOTO 100, the computer will branch straight to line 100, missing all the intervening program lines. This does not mean that those program lines are unnecessary; the GOTO statement may be an option that is executed only if a certain state of affairs exists, such as a value being more than a certain amount. Testing for certain conditions, and then branching on the results of the tests, is a very important part of most programs.

Arithmetic statements govern the calculations that take place when the program is run. In FORTRAN, these are similar to the statements of ordinary arithmetic, using plus (+), minus (−), multiplication (*), division (/), powers and brackets in the usual way. For example, to calculate the total price T of N items which cost £P each, with VAT at 17.5% added on, the statement might be written like this:

$$T = N * P * 17.5$$

Input and output statements govern the input of data into the computer and the output of the results. For example, the statement

READ (5) N, P

would tell the computer to read from device 5 (which would be some form of input device) the values given to N and P.

## 4.6 BASIC

Short for 'Beginners All-purpose Symbolic Instruction Code', BASIC was developed in the early 1960s at Dartmouth College in America as a simplified version of FORTRAN, the intention being to produce a language for teaching the principles of programming. In the early days it was a simple language, with limited use outside education, but owing to its frugal memory requirements it was adopted as the main programming language for microcomputers. Many additional commands and structures were then added to extend the language's capabilities, each microcomputer manufacturer developing his own version of BASIC.

These extensions put BASIC on a par with FORTRAN for mathematical and scientific work. However, FORTRAN was designed in the days when computers were limited in power and expensive, and so an important requirement was that it carried out its tasks efficiently and in a way that made frugal demands on the computer's power. BASIC is not a particularly efficient language, but this hardly matters now that computing power is so cheap and plentiful. Ease of use and a short learning time are more important for people who are learning programming.

Besides being designed for beginners, BASIC was intended to be 'all-purpose'. Indeed, it can be used with almost any application, from performing scientific calculations to keeping business records and controlling devices such as robot arms. However, being a general-purpose language, it is not as good for specific applications as the more specialized languages such as FORTRAN and COBOL.

On page 94 there is a short program written in BASIC. When run, it allows the user to input the unit price of a product, which it stores in memory under the variable PRICE, then input the quantity sold of the product, which it stores in memory under the variable QUANTITY. It then calculates the value of the sale and the total amount. It then calculates the VAT and displays the total. The program repeats this sequence endlessly until the user enters nothing as the price, i.e. simply presses the RETURN/ENTER key. It is quite easy to extend this program so that it produces proper invoices.

## 4.7   COBOL

COBOL is an acronym for COmmon Business Oriented Language. It was developed in 1960, at the initiative of the US Defense Department, to provide a language that was efficient at file-handling and which could therefore be applied to business-oriented applications such as stock control. One of its earliest uses was the control of inventory on US warships.

With its file-handling capabilities, COBOL quickly established itself as the major language for processing business data, and it still retains this lead in organizations which use large computers.

A COBOL program consists of four divisions. These are:

- The *identification* division, which contains information for the users of the program, but which does not affect the processing of the data.
- The *environment* division, which specifies the hardware environment – i.e. the computer system and associated devices – in which the program will run.
- The *data* division, which specifies the files to be used, the type and size of data entries, and the computer storage required.
- The *procedure* division, which lists the operations that have to be performed by the computer to process the data, such as instructions to open files, to transfer data from those files to the computer's memory, to perform calculations, and to output results.

To illustrate these operations, here's a short extract from the procedure division of a COBOL program:

```
1 OPEN-FILES.
  OPEN INPUT IN-FILE.
  OPEN OUTPUT OUT-FILE.


2 SET-RECORDS.
  MOVE SPACES TO OUT-REC.
  MOVE 1 TO 0-RECORD-TYPE.
```

3 READ-FILE-IN.
  READ IN-FILE AT END GO TO 5-FINISH.
  ADD 1 TO WS-COUNT-IN.
  MOVE IN-COPY TO OUT-COPY-1.
  READ IN-FILE AT END GO TO 8-ABORT.
  ADD 1 TO WS-COUNT-IN.
  MOVE IN-COPY TO OUT-COPY-2.

## 4.8 PROLOG

Short for PROgramming in LOGic, this language is commonly used for programming expert systems (see Chapter 6). These are systems that store human experts' knowledge on particular subjects in the form of *facts* and *rules*, and allow non-experts to ask questions which draw on that knowledge.

A fact in PROLOG is an expression of the form 'A relates to B'. Here are two examples of facts:

5 sum-of (3 2)
Lynda likes apples

A rule is a set of connected facts. Words that are used to connect facts include the logical operators AND, OR, and NOT, as well as the word IF. So a rule might be:

X likes pears if X likes apples

Using its store or *knowledge base* of facts and rules, the computer is able to deduce further facts. For example, if asked to list all people who like pears, it would include Lynda, using the fact that 'Lynda likes apples' and the rule 'X likes pears if X likes apples'.

Unlike the other languages I've mentioned, you cannot write a program in PROLOG. Its purpose is to allow you to add facts and rules to the knowledge base (using the command ADD), and to ask the computer to extract knowledge from that base in the form of inferences based on those facts and rules. To assist in this latter task, a number of query statements are available, namely statements of the form 'is (A relates to B)'.

For example, if the facts earlier in this section have been entered into the computer, the query

Is (Lynda likes apples)

will receive from the computer the reply

Yes.

As is always the case with computers, the technology comes into its own where a large amount of data is involved. If a great many facts and rules about a subject have been entered into the computer, it is possible to extract useful knowledge which would otherwise remain hidden.

### 4.9   Fourth generation programming languages

Fourth generation languages (4GLs, for short) have recently appeared. They are even further removed from the level of the machine than the third generation languages described above. With these, it is not necessary to specify *how* to carry out tasks, but *what* tasks need to be done. The detailed procedures – such as those in the rudimentary invoicing program shown in page 94 – are to a large extent generated by the language itself.

Fourth generation languages are invariably incorporated within database packages, and are used for record-keeping and other information management applications. For example, keeping records on dBASE, the world's most widely used database package, involves programming in a 4GL. Typical commands are:

LIST FOR AMOUNT > 10

which will display those records with more than £10 in the field labelled AMOUNT, and

SUM AMOUNT FOR DATE '020491'

which will add up the values of orders received on 2 April 1991.

Fourth generation languages have become popular as they cut down significantly the programming time.

## 4.10 Program generators

Programming is a time-consuming and skilled job, and the cost of writing program code can be very high. Furthermore, the programs will normally contain errors ('bugs'), and will require extensive testing to find and remove these. *Program generators*, which automatically produce the program code, are a solution to this problem.

If you use the latest version of dBASE, called dBASE IV, you can use its system of menus (the 'Control Centre') to produce record-keeping applications. You simply tell it what tasks you want carried out by selecting options from the menus, and dBASE produces the code. It takes only a few hours to learn to use the Control Centre, compared to weeks to learn to use the dBASE programming language, and it takes only a few hours to create quite complicated (and bug-free) applications using this method.

However, the Control Centre suffers from defects which are common to other program generators:

- You can't do everything from it, so for some tasks a knowledge of dBASE programming is required.
- The Control Centre does not necessarily produce the most efficient programs.

## 4.11 Programming

In business, the purpose of writing computer programs is to automate information systems within the organization. In this context, producing a computer program involves the following steps:

1  Defining the problem.
2  Designing the logic.
3  Coding.
4  Testing and debugging.
5  Writing the documentation.

Let's look at each of these.

*Defining the problem.*   This involves specifying the inputs and outputs of the system, and the data that must be stored in it. This has been dealt with already (see page 19 at the end of Chapter 1); in large organizations, problem definition is carried out by systems analysts.

*Designing the logic.*   This involves producing an *algorithm* of some sort that specifies the tasks needed to produce the outputs from the inputs and the relationships between them. An important part of this algorithm will be the branching that has to take place when various conditions are met (see page 82). One way of producing an algorithm is the *flow-chart*, described later.

*Coding.*   This involves using a high-level language (or a program generator) to produce the source program. In the case of large applications, the proposed program will have been split into modules at the algorithm stage, and each module will have its own algorithm and will be programmed separately from the others. When these modules have been tested and debugged, they will be combined to produce the final program.

*Testing and debugging.*   Each module – and the complete program – must be thoroughly tested to identify errors, and these must be removed. Sometimes, this process will take more man-hours than the original program writing. Initially, this will normally involve using the programs to process test data prepared by the systems analyst. The outputs produced are compared with the expected outputs, and any discrepancies investigated. When the program modules have been amalgamated to produce the final software, this will also need testing, to check that data is being correctly passed from one module to another. Modern software is so complex that extensive further testing is required, and users will be asked to try out the software over a period of several months and report back any problems they are experiencing. This second phase of testing is called *beta testing*.

*Documentation.*   Various kinds of documentation are needed to support business software:

- *Program documentation*, which describes the logic of the program, its division into modules, and what each step in the program is doing. This is needed to aid debugging and to facilitate future revisions of the program. Many languages allow much of this documentation to be incorporated in the program itself, in the form of *remarks*, and, if good programming practice has been followed, the overall design of the program should be such that its structure is apparent.

- The *systems overview*, which outlines for the benefit of senior management what the system will do.
- The *systems manual*, which explains in more detail the facilities that the software offers and how to use them.
- The *operating manual*, containing a list of all questions that might be asked by the computer when running the software, together with an explanation of each question and the range of acceptable operator responses.
- The *error manual*, which lists the error messages that might be produced by the system and the appropriate operator responses.

In practice, some of these manuals might be combined. When you buy an application package for PCs, the manual(s) will normally be an amalgamation of the last three, together with a tutorial guide. The all-important program documentation will have been produced, but will remain with the software house.

## 4.12 Structured programming

One of the criticisms of BASIC in its original form was its weak control structures, which mainly depended on the use of GOTO to force branching. The GOTO statement is fine for small programs. Once the program gets beyond a certain size, however, a large number of GOTO loops will become necessary, resulting in a disorganized structure that becomes very difficult to unravel. This is sometimes called 'spaghetti programming'. Furthermore, the use of GOTO to force branching means that it becomes difficult or impossible to break the program down into self-contained modules.

The programming language PASCAL, favoured by many universities and colleges as a teaching language, avoids the use of GOTO by the use of statements such as DO . . . WHILE and REPEAT . . . UNTIL. Later versions of

BASIC also incorporate these statements, and so get round the problems caused by GOTO.

Breaking down a programming problem into a set of self-contained modules is part of what's called *structured programming*. Each module can be considered as a subsystem of the wider system which is the program, and will take inputs (i.e. data) from other subsystems and will produce outputs (data) which in turn are used by other systems. The modules are therefore linked by the data that passes between them.

## 4.13    Flowcharts

I've said that flowcharts are one way of producing a program algorithm. In programming, the main flowchart symbols are

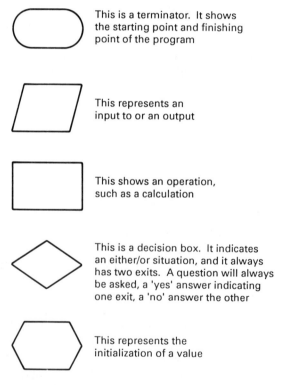

This is a terminator. It shows the starting point and finishing point of the program

This represents an input to or an output

This shows an operation, such as a calculation

This is a decision box. It indicates an either/or situation, and it always has two exits. A question will always be asked, a 'yes' answer indicating one exit, a 'no' answer the other

This represents the initialization of a value

*Figure 4.2*    Flowchart symbols

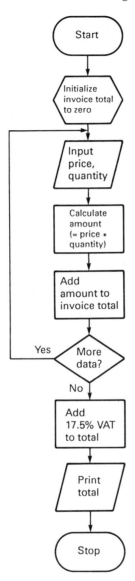

*Figure 4.3* Flowchart of simple invoicing program

as shown in Figure 4.2. Figure 4.3 shows how they might be used to produce an algorithm for a simple invoicing program. If you work through this flowchart, you will see that the program will:

- Input to the computer the price and quantity sold of an item.
- Multiply the price by the quantity to get the amount charged.
- Add this amount to the invoice total so far.
- Repeat this process for each item sold.
- When all the items have been input, add 17.5% VAT to the invoice total and print the result.

(This simple program could be easily extended to input the description of each item, and to print the description, price, quantity, and amount of each to produce something resembling a proper invoice.)

### 4.14   A BASIC program

Let's produce a program in BASIC which will carry out these flowchart steps. In this language, each line of programming must be numbered; the computer will then execute them in numbered sequence. It's conventional to number in steps of 10 (i.e. 10, 20, 30, etc.), as then additional lines can be inserted by typing intermediate numbers.

The first step in the program is to name the part of the memory in which the invoice total is to be held, and to set its initial value to 0. Let's name it simply TOTAL. TOTAL is then called a *variable*. (Note that some versions of BASIC require you to use single-character variable names, in which case we could have used 'T' as the name.) So the first program line (line 10) is:

    10 LET TOTAL = 0

Next, we tell the computer that it can expect the price and quantity of the first item on the invoice to be keyed in:

    20 INPUT PRICE, QUANTITY

What we are in fact doing here is telling the computer to label a part of its memory 'QUANTITY' and a part 'PRICE' and put the first two values that it receives (via the keyboard) into those two parts of the memory.

Next, we want the computer to calculate the AMOUNT. This will be program line 30:

30 LET AMOUNT = PRICE * QUANTITY

This tells the computer to multiply the value held at address PRICE by the value of address QUANTITY and to store the result at another address in its memory which it is to label AMOUNT.

Next, we tell the computer to add the value stored at address AMOUNT to the value at address TOTAL, and then to put the result back into TOTAL. This new value in TOTAL replaces the previous value stored there. This is line 40:

40 LET TOTAL = TOTAL + AMOUNT

We must now tell the computer to repeat this process for successive values of PRICE and QUANTITY. The 'traditional' way of doing this in BASIC is to use the GOTO command to tell it to return to line 20:

50 GOTO 20

The computer will now repeat line 20 (using the next pair of values for PRICE and QUANTITY input at the keyboard) and all successive lines to line 50.

We also need to tell the computer when it has run out of items on the invoice, i.e. when there are no more values of PRICE and QUANTITY. If we don't it will stick at line 20 looking for another pair of values when there are in fact no more, and it will never get beyond line 50. One way of telling the computer that the data has come to an end is to provide it with impossible values of PRICE and QUANTITY, such as negative values, or zero values, and to tell it to bypass line 50 when it receives these values.

Let's use zero values to tell it there are no more items on the invoice. This means that when we run the program we must key in 0 as the final value for PRICE. When the computer receives this it must bypass line 50 and go to line 60. To achieve this, we can insert after line 20 the following:

25 IF PRICE = 0 THEN GOTO 60

(Note that it does not matter that we are writing this line out of sequence, i.e. after line 50. The computer reads and executes each program line in its numerical sequence, not in the sequence in which it was keyed in.)

At line 60 we tell the computer to add 17.5% to TOTAL, and put the result back into TOTAL:

60 LET TOTAL = TOTAL * 17.5/100 + TOTAL

Then we want it to tell us what the answer is:

70 PRINT TOTAL

And the final instruction to the computer is to tell it that it has finished what we want it to do:

80 END

### 4.15   A structured program

Even in the above very short program, you can see spaghetti programming beginning to creep in with the two GOTO statements causing branching to other places. A neater and clearer way of programming would be to use the structured programming commands REPEAT . . . UNTIL. In this case, we want to REPEAT lines 20, 30 and 40 UNTIL PRICE is zero. Here's the above program rewritten in this more structured form:

```
10 LET S = 0
15 REPEAT
20 INPUT PRICE, QUANTITY
30 LET AMOUNT = PRICE * QUANTITY
40 LET TOTAL = TOTAL + AMOUNT
50 UNTIL PRICE = 0
60 LET TOTAL = TOTAL * 17.5/100 + TOTAL
70 PRINT TOTAL
80 END
```

# 5
# System software

## 5.1 What is system software?

When we apply a computer to the task of writing a letter or keeping records, we use *application software*. That application software resides in the computer's memory alongside a more basic level of software called system software. The application software does not have to tell the computer exactly how to access a disk or keyboard or control the screen display, as the system software looks after this. System software is fundamental to the computer – when you buy the computer, you also buy this software – for without it the computer can't do anything.

System software is made up of the operating system, a number of additional utilities, and, on many computers, software which provides a user-friendly operating environment.

- The *operating system* controls the disk-drives and other hardware devices and, in the case of networked computers, the network operations. It also allows you to carry out computer housekeeping tasks such as loading, copying, and deleting files.
- The *operating environment* provides an easy-to-use way of carrying out housekeeping tasks as well as providing friendly environment within which computer applications can be run.
- *Utilities* provide additional facilities and routines.

In this chapter we'll look at each of these three types of systems software. The next chapter introduces application software.

## 5.2   Operating systems

A computer's operating system enables it to carry out its disk filing and other operational tasks. We can put these tasks under five headings:

- *Basic input/output operations*, such as controlling the screen display. This is governed by the part of the operating system often known as the BIOS (Basic Input/Output System).
- *Disk operations*, which are to do with storing programs and data on disk. This is governed by the part of the operating system which on PCs is called DOS (Disk Operating System).
- *Network operations*, which enable a number of micros to be linked to each other and to share facilities such as hard disks and printers.
- *Multi-tasking*, which enable the computer to handle several tasks at the same time, such as running a record-keeping application, a spreadsheet, and a word processing program.
- *Multiuser operations*, which allow a number of people to use a computer and its software at the same time, by connecting to it other PCs or workstations.

Some operating systems on microcomputers are only able to handle the first two of these groups of tasks. As I've said, computers based on the Intel 80x86 family of microprocessors (i.e. PCs) use an operating system called *DOS*, short for 'disk operating system'. In the case of the IBM PC, its full name is *PC-DOS*, short for 'Personal computer disk operating system'; in the case of the compatible PCs from other manufacturers, its full name is *MS-DOS*, the MS being short for 'Microsoft', the software house that wrote DOS. In spite of the differences in name, the two products are, for all practical purposes, identical. DOS was developed from the earlier CP/M operating system used on Z80-based microcomputers.

Over the years, DOS has grown steadily more powerful, and has passed through several versions or 'levels'. Each version has added features which support new hardware developments, such as the ability to handle hard disks, 3.5

inch disks, and so on. The current version is level 4. The version designed for the IBM PS/2 microcomputers is called OS/2, and this supports multitasking.

Digital Research Corporation, which is Microsoft's main competitor, sells a competing operating system for PCs called Concurrent DOS. This offers the following features:

- Multitasking with up to four 'windows' visible at any time on the screen, each running a different program.
- Multiuser facilities for up to three users, using PCs or workstations linked to an IBM-AT or compatible.
- Compatibility with DOS, so that programs written for that operating system will run without difficulty.

A more powerful operating system, which runs on larger computers and also on more powerful PCs (i.e. those based on the 80386 chip and above), is *Unix*. This is designed with multitasking and multiuser applications in mind, and is steadily increasing in popularity as microcomputers become more powerful and more capable of operating in these modes. It is worth noting that the 'Helios' operating system being developed for the new generation of transputer-based computers is based upon Unix.

Other types of computer use different operating systems. For example, the 680x0 based Atari ST uses the *TOS* operating system.

### 5.3 How the operating system organizes the disk

Storing, organizing, and retrieving files are central tasks for all operating systems. To understand these systems, it is therefore necessary to know something of the principles of disk filing. This is covered in the sections below.

First, note that each file, whether it is a program file supplied by a software house or a data or text file that you have produced, is given a name. That name, together with the location of the file on the disk, is stored in the index, a special area on the disk's surface. When you type the filename, the operating system looks it up in the index, locates the file, and loads it into RAM.

## 5.4   Directories

Because a hard disk can hold many hundreds or thousands of files, it is necessary to organize them into separate sections in the index. These sections are called *directories*, and they act rather like the sections in a library, separating files by subject matter or use. For example, the word processing software that you use may be held in one directory, and your record-keeping software in another. The text or data files that you create may be held in the same directories as the software, or you may find it convenient to house them in other directories.

(Floppy disks have a limited storage capacity and can therefore hold only a limited number of files. In this case it is not necessary to organize the files into directories, and operating systems that were developed before hard disks appeared – such as CP/M – are not able to handle directories.)

Directories are organized into what's called a *tree structure*. To appreciate what this means, think of a directory as the branch of a tree:

- As a branch has leaves, so a directory has files.
- As a branch splits off into smaller branches which have their own leaves, so a directory may contain other subdirectories, each with their own files.

The basic directory which contains all other directories is called the *root* directory.

Figure 5.1 shows part of the directory structure of my hard disk. As you can see, I've called one of the directories QA, as this contains Q&A, the software package that I sometimes use for word processing and record keeping. This directory contains two subdirectories called DATA and TEXT; these hold the data files (for the record-keeping part of Q&A) and the text files (for the word processing part) respectively. Because I have so many text files, I find it convenient to have several subdirectories within TEXT, to separate out letters, files created by my wife, and so on. These are shown in the figure.

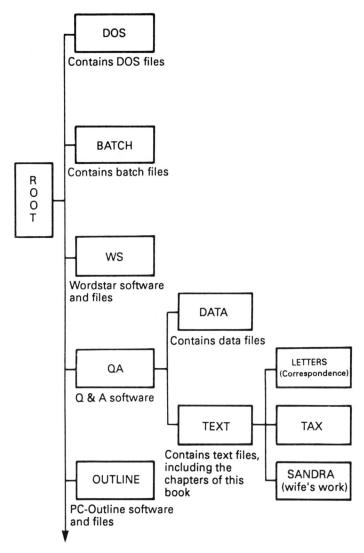

*Figure 5.1* Part of the directory system on my hard disk

## 5.5 Naming files

To distinguish individual files within a directory, they must be given unique names. In many operating systems, including DOS, a filename consists of two parts: the stem (the main part of the name) and an extension, separated by a dot. In CP/M and DOS, the stem can be up to 8 characters long, and the extension can be up to 3 characters long. You can use the stem to identify the contents of the file, and you may be able to use the extension to identify what type or class of file it is.

Most software dictates what the extension must be. For example, GrandView (the software I am using to write this book) adds the extension .GV to all files created by it. So the filename of this chapter is CHAP5.GV – I provided the stem, GrandView imposed the extension. (This file is in the directory of my hard disk called GV, along with the GrandView program files.)

In the case of program files, the operating system dictates the extension:

- In DOS and CP/M you can write your own batch program files to automatically execute batches of operating system commands (see your operating system manual), and you must give these the extension BAT.
- Some system files (i.e. files which are connected with the operating system) must have the extension SYS.
- Some program files must have the extension COM (short for command).
- Other program files must have the extension EXE (short for executable).

To run BAT, SYS, COM, and EXE files you can omit the extension and merely type the stem of the name. If there is a file of that name on the disk with one of these extensions, DOS or CP/M will run it.

## 5.6 Operating system commands

Although operating systems differ in their capabilities, some offering more facilities than others, they all perform the same types of tasks. Furthermore, many operating systems use similar commands, examples being the command COPY to copy a file, DELETE or DEL to delete a file, RENAME to rename a file, and, in the case of a program file, the file name itself in order to execute (i.e. run) it. In the following sections I shall deal with the main concepts and commands that are common to most systems. If you wish, you can bypass these and go straight to the section on operating environments on page 106.

As you read these sections, note the following points.

1   If you use a BBC micro, you must type a '*' before each of these commands, to tell the computer that you wish to step outside BASIC into the operating system.
2   You can type operating system commands in either upper or lower case. However, to help you to distinguish commands from other text in this chapter, I will use upper case throughout.
3   Many DOS commands incorporate a number of options, and you select which you want by:

●   First typing the symbol '/' after the command.
●   Then typing a letter specifying the option.

These options are called *switches*, for they allow you to switch the command to a different mode. For example, the DIR command, described below, which lists filenames down the left of the screen, can be switched to list them across the width of the screen by means of the 'W' switch:

    DIR/W

## 5.7   Setting the current drive

Most microcomputer systems have two disk drives, which will be either a hard disk drive and one floppy, or two floppy drives. Many operating systems identify each drive by a letter: the first floppy drive is called Drive A, the second floppy drive is called Drive B, and the hard disk is called Drive C. If you are using a BBC micro, the drives are numbered 0, 1, etc.

The computer can only concentrate its attention on one drive at a time; the one that it is currently looking at is called the *current* drive. In the case of DOS or CP/M, when you turn the computer on the drive containing the operating system files will be the current drive; this will normally be either Drive C or, in the case of a system without a hard disk, drive A.

To change the current drive in DOS or CP/M, you simply type the drive letter followed by a colon. For example,

    A:

will make the first floppy drive current, and

    C:

will set the hard disk current.

## 5.8   Displaying the contents of a directory

The directory that you are in when you first power up the computer or switch drives is the root directory of the current disk. To display its contents (i.e. the files and subdirectories that it contains) you must enter the command

    DIR

(which is short for 'directory'). Note that on some systems, such as the BBC micro, the command is CAT (which is short for 'catalogue'). This lists the filenames down the screen.

## 5.9   Changing directories

To tell the computer to change its attention to a subdirectory within the current directory, the DOS command is CHDIR (short for 'change directory') followed by the name of the directory. Other systems may have slight variations. Under DOS, you can abbreviate this command to just:

    CD <followed by the directory name>

So if I want to change from the root directory to the QA directory in order to run the Q&A software, I type

CD QA

If I want to go down a further level to the TEXT subdirectory of the QA directory (see Figure 5.1), I must enter the further command

CD TEXT

It's easier, though, to combine both of these in a single command. To do this in DOS, type CD followed by both QA and TEXT, separated by a backslash:

CD QA\TEXT

This changes first to the QA directory, and then the TEXT subdirectory within QA.

Other systems may use symbols other than the backslash. Some, for instance, use the ordinary slash '/', while the Acorn Econet system uses a dot.

## 5.10   Changing to the root directory

The root directory is unique, for it is the start of the directory tree. Under DOS, it is designated by the single character '\', and if you type

CD\

you will jump from wherever you are on the directory tree to the root directory.

By combining this '\' with other directory names, you can move directly from a subdirectory in one part of the directory tree to another subdirectory in a quite different part. For example, if I am in the BATCH directory on my hard disk, I can move straight to the TEXT subdirectory within the QA directory by typing

CD\QA\TEXT

## 5.11   Renaming, copying, and deleting files

The DOS command to rename a file is

RENAME <old filename> <new filename>

For example, if, on my hard disk, the \QA\TEXT directory is current, I can rename CHAP4.IT as CHAPTER4 by typing

RENAME CHAP4.IT CHAPTER4

If I am in some other directory, I will have to enter what's called the *pathname*, which is the full directory route to the file plus the filename:

RENAME\QA\TEXT\CHAP4.IT CHAPTER4

A file called CHAP4.IT will no longer appear in the listing of this directory, being replaced by an identical file called CHAPTER4.

The DOS command to copy a file is COPY followed by the existing filename and the new filename. For example, if I am in the TEXT subdirectory of the QA directory,

COPY CHAP4.IT CHAPTER4

will create a duplicate of CHAP4.IT with the name CHAPTER4.

The copy command is often used to create duplicates of hard-disk files on a floppy disk, to be stored away in a safe place in case of fire or other disaster. For example, if I am in the root directory of my hard disk, I can copy this chapter by issuing the command:

COPY\QA\TEXT\CHAP4.IT A:

This will create a copy of the same name on Drive A. If I want to use a different name for my copy, for example CHAPTER4, the command is

COPY\QA\TEXT\CHAP4.IT A:CHAPTER4

The DOS command to delete a file is DEL followed by the filename.

Similar commands are used to perform these tasks in other operating systems.

## 5.12 Wildcards

A *wildcard*, in computer jargon, is a symbol which, when used in a filename, can represent any character or group of characters at that position in the name. You use wildcards to select all files with the same extension, or with similar stems, so that you can copy or delete a whole group of files with a single command.

The most useful wildcard symbol is *. If you include this in a filename, you are telling the operating system that any character or group of characters can occupy that position or any of the remaining positions in the stem of the name or in the extension. For example:

    *.GV

says to the operating system, 'all files with the extension GV', and

    CHAP*.GV

says to the operating system, 'all files with the extension GV and with stems beginning with CHAP', and

    *.*

says to the operating system, 'all files with any stem and any extension'.

So I can type the following command to delete all the files in the current directory on the floppy disk in Drive A:

    DEL A:*.*

To copy all the chapters of a book from my hard disk to this floppy, the command is:

COPY C:\QA\TEXT\CHAP*.IT A:

## 5.13   Making and removing directories

The DOS command to make a directory is MKDIR followed by the directory name. This can be shortened to MD:

MD MYDIR

creates the directory MYDIR within the current directory. Note that, like DOS filenames, a directory name cannot exceed 8 characters in length.

To remove a directory, the DOS command is RMDIR. This can be shortened to RD:

RD MYDIR

will remove the directory MYDIR in the current directory. Note that to use this command, you must first delete all files (and subdirectories) in the directory you wish to remove.

These are just some of the operating system commands. For others, such as commands to format a floppy disk or to backup a disk, see the operating system manual for your computer.

## 5.14   Operating environments

DOS and most other operating systems are not 'user friendly'. The commands that you read about in the last section are awkward to memorize and use, and if you are not familiar with the computer keyboard they are awkward to type. Also, the computer screen with its enigmatic C: is rather unfriendly and difficult to come to terms with, and most people appreciate something that resembles more closely the familiar world of the office with its drawers, folders, waste-paper basket, and so on.

Hence the need for *operating environments*, software which sits on top of the operating system and presents us with an easy-to-use and friendly way of performing the kind of tasks described above. The two most popular operating environments on microcomputers are:

1   The Apple Macintosh operating environment and the almost identical *GEM* from Digital Research. GEM is short for 'Graphics Environment Manager', and it is available on the Atari ST, PC-compatibles, and some other micros.
2   *Windows* from Microsoft, available for all PC-compatibles, though best used on 80386 models and above. This is virtually identical to *Presentation Manager* (PM), used on the IBM PS/2 range of micros.

Both the Macintosh/GEM environment and Windows/PM have many similarities, for they are both based on the earlier operating environment developed by Xerox at the end of the 1970s. (As was explained on page 49, the Apple Mac popularized this environment.) In the future, this way of working is likely to become common across computers of every kind.

Xerox's original product – which was never released commercially – grew out of painstaking research into the way in which people interact with computers. Pressing the arrow keys on the keyboard to move around the screen, for instance, is not very efficient or natural, and so the mouse was developed. Pushing this across your desk produces corresponding movements of the cursor on the screen. Selecting files or software options by typing at the keyboard is also unnatural and inefficient, so a button is provided at the front of the mouse. Now, to make your selection, you merely push the mouse to move to the file or the option displayed on the screen, and click the button. In the case of a software program, you run it by 'double clicking', i.e. pressing the button twice in quick succession.

Xerox's research also showed that most people find the conventional text-based display unfriendly and difficult to use, preferring instead one that was graphics based. In this, pictures or *icons* represent the functions and tasks of the system, examples being a picture of a wastepaper basket to represent the delete function for getting rid of files, a filing drawer to represent a disk-drive, and so on. The cursor itself is represented by an icon, normally an arrow to point to files or functions.

Even files are represented by icons, namely minature sheets of paper containing the filenames, and directories are represented by pictures of folders. The contents of a directory appear in a box or 'window' on the screen. Several directories can be displayed at the same time in different windows, and files can be copied from one to another simply by selecting them with the mouse, keeping the button held down, and 'dragging' them to another window.

Other facilities include:

- *Pull-down menus.*   The menus are listed across the top of the screen, and a menu's options appear as a list below it when you point to it with the mouse. To select an option, you point and click with the mouse.
- *Dialogue boxes.*   These appear in situations where you need to turn a number of options on or off, or type in something like a filename. To set an option, you mouse-click on a 'radio button' located alongside it (see Figure 5.2).

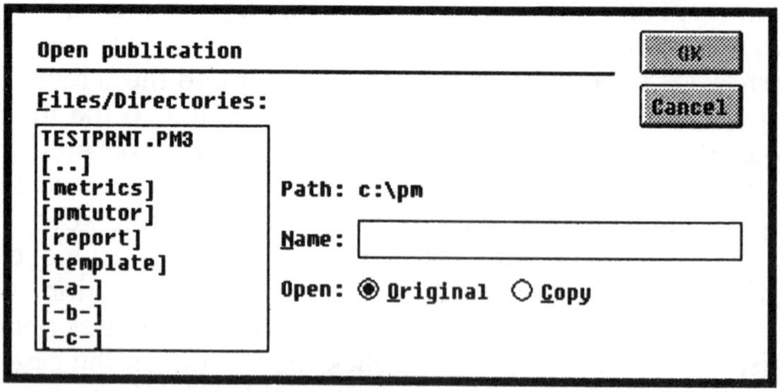

*Figure 5.2*   Example of a dialogue box

This kind of interface is called a *graphical user interface*, or GUI. The term WIMP is also used, meaning 'Window, Icon, Mouse, Pointer'.

In the future, it is likely that more advanced computer environments will appear. Work is currently being done on developing an animated icon – which might look like a human being but could be configured in any way the user chooses – that can converse with the user using speech synthesis and speech recognition. The icon will be linked to an expert system (see page 147) and so will seem 'intelligent', able to guide the user through the system. Another example is the electronic stylus, being developed for annotating documents on screen.

## 5.15 GEM

Figure 5.3 shows a GEM display, with a window showing the contents of the root directory of the disk in Drive A. Note the slide bar at the right of the window, which you can use to scroll through the contents of the directory. The procedure is to 'point' to it with the mouse (i.e. move the arrow on the screen to it), hold down the mouse button, and 'drag' it to a new position.

Quite a number of applications programs are able to run within the GEM or Windows environments. This means that they do not take over the entire screen but instead carry out their tasks within the confines of a window, and are therefore able to take advantage of facilities such as scroll bars and pull-down menus.

The opening display that appears on the screen when you run GEM (or the equivalent product on the Apple Mac, or indeed Windows) is called the Desktop. In the Mac and GEM environments it contains:

- Icons representing the disk drives available on the system, e.g. Drive A and Drive C.
- An icon representing a trash-can, used for deleting files.
- Functions listed across the top, which, when selected, reveal pull-down menus.

From the Desktop you can perform one or more of the operations listed below. In these operations much use is made of windows. You can open several windows on the screen at the same time, each one showing different information. The one in which you are currently working is called the *active* window, and it may partly obscure other windows. You can open windows, close windows, expand or contract

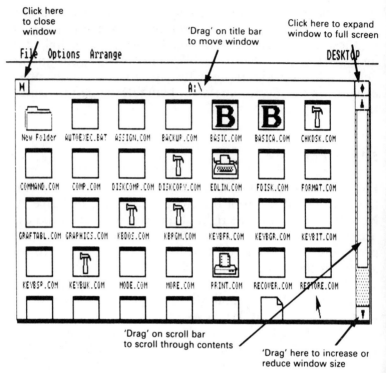

Click here
to close
window

'Drag' on title bar
to move window

Click here to expand
window to full screen

File  Options  Arrange                                    DESKTOP

'Drag' on scroll bar
to scroll through contents

'Drag' here to increase or
reduce window size

*Figure 5.3*   A GEM display

windows, and move windows around the screen. How you
do this is explained below.

(Note that the latest version of GEM Desktop on the PC
has had a number of these features removed. If you use
GEM on a PC, it is worth getting hold of the pre-October
1986 version of GEM Desktop. GEM on the Atari ST and
the Apricot F2 works as described below, as does the pre-
86 version on the PC and the virtually identical system on
the Apple Mac.)

1  *Open a drawer.*   One operation is opening a 'drawer',
   i.e. displaying a catalogue of the contents of one of the
   drives. You do this by using the mouse to move the
   pointer to the drive icon and double-clicking. A window
   appears on the screen, displaying the catalogue in icon
   form, as shown in Figure 5.3. Each file in the root

directory is represented by a miniature sheet of paper with the file name on it, and the directories are represented by folders. If you now click on the other drive, to display its calalogue, a second window appears on the screen, overlapping the first, with folders and sheets shown in it. This is now the active window. To close the active window, and return to the previous one, you click on the 'close box' icon at the top left corner of the window.

2  *Select a function.*   Another operation is selecting one of the functions listed across the top of the screen. You do this by moving the pointer to it, an action which results in the appearance on the screen of the pull-down menu for that function, then moving the pointer down the menu list and clicking on the option you require.

3  *Move an icon.*   A third option is moving an icon to a different position on the screen. You do this by moving the pointer to the icon, holding down the left-hand button, and 'dragging' the icon to a new position.

4  *Manipulate a window.*   In a similar way you can alter the size of, and move, the disk catalogue windows. You alter a window's size by clicking on and dragging the symbol shown in its bottom right-hand corner, and you move it by clicking on and dragging the title bar at the top. (In this way you can arrange the Desktop to look the way you want it, and then save your configuration – using the 'Save Desktop' option – so that it automatically appears the next time you run GEM.) Also, if the window is too small to display all its contents, you can 'scroll' through those contents in both horizontal and vertical directions by either clicking on the arrows or dragging the scroll bars displayed at the bottom and at the right of the window.

Most of your work with the Desktop will, of course, be to perform the sort of operations described in the section on DOS earlier in this chapter, such as running applications, changing directories, and copying, deleting, and performing other operations on files. All these are carried out by moving the pointer and clicking.

For example:

- To open a folder, i.e. select a directory and catalogue its contents, you click on its icon. A new set of icons appears in the active window, representing the contents of the selected directory.
- To close a folder, and return to the previous directory, you click on the 'close box' icon in the top left corner of the window.
- To run an application, you click on its icon. This will resemble a sheet of paper, with the name of the application attached.
- To delete a file, you drag its icon to the trash can, and click on the confirmation message that appears.
- To copy a file from one disk to another you drag it to the drive icon you wish to copy to. To copy a file from one directory to a second directory, you drag it to the folder representing the second directory.

These, and other basic DOS tasks, can also be carried out on whole groups of files and on directories, much more quickly and easily than is possible using the ordinary DOS system of commands. For example, to delete a whole group of files from a directory, you hold down SHIFT while clicking on each file in turn, and then, with SHIFT still held down, drag the lot to the trash can.

### 5.16   Running applications within the Mac/GEM environments

As indicated above, to run an application from the desktop you simply click on the icon that represents it. On the PC, most software that you run from GEM Desktop will take over the screen, and will not use any of the mouse, icon, scroll bars, and pop-down menu features that GEM provides. You will not in fact be aware that GEM is lying dormant in the background until you leave the application, when you will be returned to the desktop. However, some applications are specially written to run within the GEM environment, and these make full use of GEM's facilities.

On the Atari ST, almost all software is designed to use GEM's facilities, and one of the main features of the Apple

Mac is the fact that all applications adopt the mouse-and-icon way of working.

## 5.17 Windows

Early versions of Windows were much inferior to the Mac/GEM environment, and little application software was written to take advantage of this environment. With version 3, released in 1990, Windows has become a fully-fledged graphical user interface. Its desktop somewhat resembles the Mac/GEM Desktop, with scroll bars, pull-down menus, icons, dialogue boxes, etc. The virtually identical product for the PS/2, Presentation Manager, appeared a couple of years earlier.

Although it arrived late on the scene, Windows 3 is much more powerful than GEM, as it overcomes the two main limitations of (the current version of) the PC's operating system, DOS:

- It breaks the 640K memory barrier, allowing Windows applications to use up to 32 Mb.
- It provides multitasking facilities, i.e. it can run several applications at the same time, each within a different window. This multitasking capability is very potent, for it allows you to switch instantly from one task to another, to copy data rapidly from one to another, and to carry out one job while another is being processed in the background.

Note that these facilities are only fully available on PCs using the 80386 processor and above. PCs with lower specifications can use only some of the power of Windows. In addition, Windows may run so slowly on cheaper machines that it loses its appeal. (Alternative operating environments are available for low-cost PCs – see later.)

Windows also offers a number of other powerful features, including *Dynamic Data Exchange* (DDE). This allows data to be copied from one Windows application to another, and the link that is thus created between the two applications kept 'live'. This means that if the data is changed in one application, these changes are automatically updated in the other.

At the time of writing, Windows v.3 has only recently appeared. However, it is growing rapidly in popularity, a number of applications have appeared which make use of its features, and a very large number of Windows applications are in the pipeline. (As with GEM, non-Windows applications take over the screen, leaving Windows in the background.) There seems little doubt that by the mid-1990s it will be the main way of working on PCs.

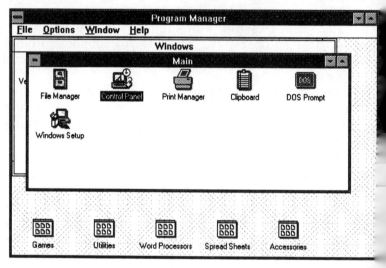

*Figure 5.4* The Windows Desktop

Presentation Manager, in contrast, has relatively few applications written for it, the result being that it has so far (i.e. by 1990) had hardly any impact on the world of microcomputing. This may change in the future, however. As people get used to Windows on PCs they may well migrate to the more powerful PS/2 hardware platform running the almost identical PM.

## 5.18   Other environments for PCs

You can have multitasking, access to large amounts o memory, and a mouse-and-windows environment, withou resorting to running Windows on a high-specification PC. One environment that will give you all these things and yet which will run on the lowliest 8086 machine is DesqView, from Quarterdeck.

DesqView is not a graphical user interface, so it does not use icons. It is character-based. The term COW (Character-Oriented Windows) is applied to software that is character-based but uses the mouse and windows. Like GUI environments, COW software includes devices such as pull-down menus and dialogue boxes from which you can make selections using the mouse. Its advantage over GUI software is the speed at which it runs, even on low-spec PCs.

GrandView (Figure 5.5), the package I am using for writing this book, is COW software, and it's one of the fastest packages I've ever used. For ordinary tasks like writing text or keeping records there is little point in graphical user interface, as no graphics are involved. (If I were desktop publishing this book, however, I would want a GUI.) Another popular COW package is PC Tools (version 5 and above), from Central Point Software.

## 5.19 Utilities

The third category of system software is utilities. These enable you to extend the power of the operating system, by:

- Carrying out tasks which are beyond the capabilities of the operating system.
- Carrying out operating system tasks in a more efficient and easier way.

Some utilities are designed to carry out one job only, such as restoring files that have been deleted in error. Others provide a computer housekeeping environment, enabling you to carry out housekeeping tasks as easily as in GEM or Windows, and from which you can run applications. The latter may include facilities which are lacking in GEM and Windows, such as options to hide files so that they cannot be listed, to protect files so that they cannot be altered or deleted, and so on.

However, unlike the Mac/GEM or Windows environ-

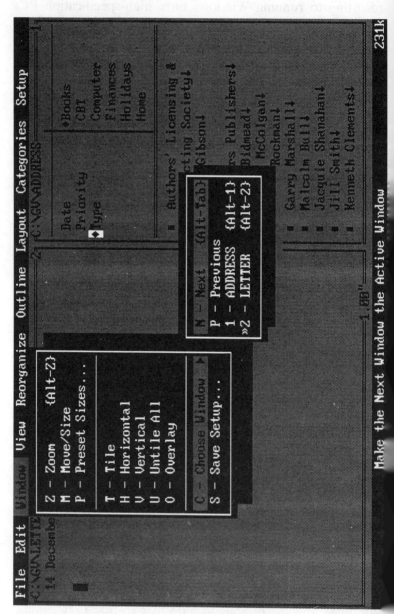

*Figure 5.5*    GrandView, an example of COW software

*Figure 5.6* PowerMenu, an example of a front-end to DOS

ments, you cannot run applications from within this type of software; you must run them from the operating system itself. All that this software does is provide an easy access to the operating system's facilities, together with a menu of some kind that enables you to run applications from within the operating system. For this reason they are called *front-ends* (to the operating system) rather than environments.

Popular front-ends to DOS are PowerMenu (Figure 5.6), PC Tools, Qdos, and Xtree.

# 6
# Application software

## 6.1    What is an application package?

We've covered the main types of system software, so let's turn now to application software. This is the software that enables us to do the things that we bought our computer for, such as playing games, writing music, creating animated displays, or administering the office.

Application software is normally supplied as a *package*, consisting of:

* The software, supplied on floppy disks.
* One or more manuals, explaining how to use the software.
* A tutorial, supplied either on disk, or in a booklet, or both.

PC-compatibles are supported by thousands of software packages. Most of these are reasonably priced. Many are free, being available in what is known as the *public domain*. Public domain (PD) software is normally available from user groups, one being Compulink at Guildford in Surrey. The manual for a PD product is normally supplied as a text file on the same disk as the software, and has to be printed out by the user.

The Apple Macintosh is also well supported by application software, much of it highly innovative and excellently designed, though there is not so much of it as for the PC. The Atari ST is quite well supported, notably by games, graphics applications such as computer-aided design, and music.

This chapter and the next cover the subject of application

software, and describe the main types of business applications running on personal computers. There are additional considerations when dealing with the kind of large applications that run on mainframes, and these are dealt with in Chapter 9.

## 6.2   The main application areas

The main areas in which computers are applied are:

- Data processing (described in Chapter 9).
- Office automation (described in this chapter and Chapter 7).
- Manufacturing and retailing (dealt with in Chapters 10 and 11).
- Education and leisure (covered in Chapter 7 and also in Chapter 11).

The kinds of application packages that are available include:

- Record-keeping software.
- Spreadsheet software.
- Word processing software.
- Desktop publishing software.
- Business graphics and presentations software.
- Communications software.
- Project planning software.
- Diary systems and other personal productivity tools.
- Expert systems software.
- Drawing and computer-aided design software.
- Computer-aided manufacturing software.
- Games.
- Music synthesis.
- Painting and animation software.

Some packages can perform more than one of these tasks. For example, there are a number of office administration packages that will carry out word processing, record-keeping, spreadsheets, and business graphics. These are called *integrated* packages, because they integrate, or bring together, these varied tasks. Some of them are remarkably cheap, one example for the PC being Ability, from Migent, costing just under £100. A more powerful integrated package which is very popular is Smart, which costs several hundred pounds.

### 6.3 Features of application packages

Most application packages have the following features.

- They may be *command-driven*, or *menu-driven*, or a combination of both. To illustrate what this means, DOS is command-driven, so that you have to learn a number of commands to use it, which you then type in. Windows and GEM, in contrast, are menu-driven, so that you merely have to select menu options to use their facilities. Command-driven software takes longer to learn, but gives you greater flexibility.
- They often provide *context-sensitive help*. This means that by pressing a certain key – usually the function key F1 – a screen or more of text appears that gives guidance on the option you have selected or the task you are carrying out.
- When using them, you normally *create a file* of data, text, or graphics, which you will want to save on disk for use with the software on a subsequent occasion. The package will contain the necessary routines to save and load files, which you invoke either by typing a command or selecting a menu option.
- Although most packages will store the data, text, or image files in their own special formats, many will also allow you to save the files in a standard format (e.g. ASCII in the case of text files) and to load files that have been so saved. This means that files created on one package can be *imported* into another, with certain limitations (such as loss of emboldening and other text enhancements in the case of ASCII files).
- When using a software package, you may want to *print your work*. Most packages will allow you to adapt the output for your particular printer. All you have to do is

select the printer from the list that is supported by the software.

## 6.4   Macro languages

Many application packages allow you to add your own custom features by means of *macros*. A macro is a stored sequence of keystrokes and other commands that can be replayed at will, usually by pressing Ctrl or Alt and another key.

The simplest type of macro language consists just of keystrokes, which you record merely by pressing the keys while the package is in macro-recording mode. Alternatively, you can create the macro by typing the commands that generate the keystrokes on a macro editing screen. For example, the command <rgt> in some macro languages is equivalent to pressing the right arrow, <F6> is equivalent to pressing the F6 key, and so on.

A number of applications provide very sophisticated macro languages, often similar to PASCAL or BASIC, which include file commands, IF . . . THEN constructions, logical operators, and so on. Macros written in these can be very powerful, allowing you to customize the whole operation and appearance of the package. For example, in some packages you can use the macro language to create customized menu systems so that the application becomes dedicated to a particular task or range of tasks, shielding the user from the packages's other complexities. Some of these more powerful macro languages are called *scripting languages*. They include the Hyperscript language available on the Wingz spreadsheet and Hypertalk available on the Apple HyperCard package.

Unfortunately, most macro languages have little in common, apart from a general similarity to a programming language such as PASCAL. This means that the user who wants to customize several different packages will have to master the macro language of each. Moves are afoot however, to try to bring some order and standardization into this situation. In the Windows world of the PC Microsoft is developing a BASIC-like scripting language that will control multiple Windows applications. Apple is bringing out its AppleScript language which will perform similar function in its environment.

## 6.5   Example of an application package

If you have access to an IBM PC or compatible computer, one example of a simple application package is *Homebase*. I've chosen to describe Homebase because:

- It is available as shareware, so anyone can try it free of charge.
- It is an example of *personal productivity software*, described later in this chapter.
- It is simple to describe and use, since it provides only a limited range of facilities. (PC Tools, for example, is a much more powerful piece of software.)
- It uses keys such as Esc, Tab, and F1 in much the same way as most standard PC application packages.

Homebase enables you to carry out, in a very neat and simple way, a range of tasks on your computer from record keeping to word processing. It is *RAM-resident*, meaning that it sits in the background in your computer's RAM, letting you get on with your other computing tasks, until you need it. Then, at the press of a key, it pops up on the screen ready for action, and at the press of another key, it disappears, returning you to your original task. This type of software is also called *terminate-and-stay-resident* (TSR), as when you quit it and return to your other task it remains resident in the computer's memory.

When you load Homebase into your computer, nothing happens to begin with. Its facilities are all dormant until you bring them to life by pressing special *hot key* combinations. You hold down the ALT key and the SHIFT key and then press another key. As a general rule you will want to run another application alongside Homebase, and by pressing a hot key call up a Homebase facility within that application as and when you need it.

Each Homebase module has a similar feel. It offers a list of menu options across the top of the screen which work in the same way as the menu system used in many other software packages:

- You select a menu option by either moving the highlight bar to it by pressing the right or left arrow key, then pressing ENTER, or by pressing the first letter of the option's name.

- If you use the first of these methods, then, as the highlight bar passes over a menu option, a one-line list of its facilities appears immediately below. This is very useful for the new or occasional user.

- Pressing the F1 key gives you context-sensitive help, i.e. a screen of text explaining how to use the current menu option.

- When you call up a menu option, it appears in a window on the screen, the size and position of which can be adjusted to suit your taste. Some options involve several windows, and you can step through the windows by pressing the TAB key.

- To cancel the last option, press the ESCAPE key. Repeatedly pressing ESC takes you backwards through your route through the Homebase menu system, eventually returning you to the point at which you invoked Homebase in your original applications. Alternatively, pressing ALT-SHIFT-ENTER or ALT-SHIFT-ESC returns you immediately to your application; in this case, the computer remembers where you left off in Homebase and takes you to it when you press the appropriate hot-key combination.

One of Homebase's modules, for example, is its calendar (Figure 6.1). To activate this, you press ALT and SHIFT and C at the same time. The calendar then pops up on the screen. This is in fact both a weekly/monthly calendar and a diary. If you select the monthly calendar, it displays a single month, highlighting the current day. You can move from day to day using the arrow keys, or from month to month by pressing PgUp or PgDn. Pressing ENTER displays the diary entry for the highlighted day. The weekly calendar is similar, though in this case the times of any appointments (though not the appointment details) are highlighted in each day's box.

You enter details of your appointments in the diary mode. You can also enter expenses against each entry, and the diary will keep an automatic total. There is a 'To Do' section for each day, in which you can enter tasks that do not have to be done at specific times, like finishing off a report for

```
CALENDAR : Daily Calendar: Return   Monthly: CTRL M          12:03a 17
   Month: PgUp PgDn, Year: ^PgUp ^PgDn
                                             F1 for help - Esc to exit
```

```
   June                      STAFF HOLIDAYS                      1937
   Sun  5/31   Mon  6/1   Tue  6/2   Wed  6/3   Thu  6/4   Fri  6/5   Sat  6/6

     8:00a      8:00a      8:00a      8:00a      8:00a      8:00a      8:00a
     9:00a      9:00a      9:00a      9:00a      9:00a      9:00a      9:00a
    10:00a     10:00a     10:00a     10:00a     10:00a     10:00a     10:00a
    11:00a     11:00a     11:00a     11:00a     11:00a     11:00a     11:00a
    12:00p     12:00p     12:00p     12:00p     12:00p     12:00p     12:00p
     1:00p      1:00p      1:00p      1:00p      1:00p      1:00p      1:00p
     2:00p      2:00p      2:00p      2:00p      2:00p      2:00p      2:00p
     3:00p      3:00p      3:00p      3:00p      3:00p      3:00p      3:00p
     4:00p      4:00p      4:00p      4:00p      4:00p      4:00p      4:00p
     5:00p      5:00p      5:00p      5:00p      5:00p      5:00p      5:00p
     6:00p      6:00p      6:00p      6:00p      6:00p      6:00p      6:00p
     7:00p      7:00p      7:00p      7:00p      7:00p      7:00p      7:00p
     8:00p      8:00p      8:00p      8:00p      8:00p      8:00p      8:00p
    LATER      LATER      LATER      LATER      LATER      LATER      LATER
```

*Figure 6.1*   The Homebase calendar

the boss, digging the garden, fixing that shelf, etc. At the end of each week or other period of time you can roll all the 'To Do' items forward, and be reminded of any that you haven't yet done. There is also a 'Find' option which allows you to enter a name or other word and will search through the diary for appointments containing it. So you can quickly check dates and times of meetings.

Other Homebase modules include a calculator, a simple word processor, a record-keeping program, and a communications program.

## 6.6   Office automation software

The term *office automation* (OA) is used to describe the application of the computer to the work of the office, i.e. the work of the manager, administrator, secretary, and office assistant. The automation of office tasks has happened only recently, within the last 10 or 15 years.

Factory automation has long been a feature of the industrial scene, and large equipment feeding huge production lines has boosted the productivity of factory workers and created much of the wealth of the industrialized world. The automation of routine clerical jobs such as payroll, stock control, invoicing, purchase records, and financial accounting procedures has also been going on for a long time, ever since the introduction of large and expensive punched card equipment early in this century.

The reason why the world of the manager, the administrator, and the secretary has been so long unaffected by these developments is simply that the equipment was so large and expensive that it could only be economically used for large routine jobs with long production runs – such as generating hundreds of invoices or thousands of payslips – which is not what the jobs of managers and secretaries are about. Their jobs are very varied. Managers' jobs involve getting information together from many sources in order to make decisions on a variety of topics, and putting those decisions into effect. Secretaries' jobs involve a variety of supporting activities such as writing letters, keeping diaries, and making appointments.

The automation of highly varied jobs of this sort had to await the advent of low-cost microcomputers that could economically be used for small-run office jobs, supported by spreadsheet, word processing, diary management and other office software. The most popular microcomputers for office automation are PCs, though Apple Macs are quite widely used for desktop publishing and graphics applications.

The main types of software used for office automation applications are:

- Database software for record-keeping applications.
- Spreadsheet software for applications involving tables of data.
- Business graphics software for presentations.
- Word processing and desktop publishing software for letters, brochures, etc.
- Communications software for electronic mail and to access on-line databases.
- Personal productivity software, such as diary systems and electronic notepads.
- Other software, such as project planning and expert systems.

All these are dealt with in the sections below, apart from graphics and desktop publishing software (covered in Chapter 7), and communications software (covered in Chapter 8). In most sections, I shall adopt the following general pattern, which will be to:

- Introduce the application.
- Discuss the main concepts underlying the application.
- Outline the main tasks that have to be done.
- Describe how the application is used in practice.

## 6.7 Database software

A *database* is a set of data organized into records. A software package which allows you to organize data in this way is called a *database management system* (DBMS). There are two types of database software:

- Packages which are able to handle just one file of records at a time, sometimes called *cardbox* or *flat-file* packages.
- *Relational* database packages, which are able to handle several files at a time, and to build links (or relationships) between files.

Relational databases are needed for more complex applications. One such application is invoicing, where customer details (such as the name and address) have to be extracted from the customer file, and product details (such as the price) have to be extracted from the stock file (see below). Relational databases can be (and often are) used for single-file applications, but, being more complex than flat-file packages, they may make those applications unnecessarily difficult.

To illustrate the difference between flat-file and relational databases, I'll enlarge on the invoicing application mentioned in the last paragraph. This may have two main files:

- The customer file, which has one record per customer with his or her name and address, and onto which you enter details of all orders received from customers – the products purchased, the price, the date of purchase, and so on.
- The product file, which has one record per product line, holding details such as the price, quantities received from suppliers and dates, quantities issued to customers and dates, the balance in stock and so on.

You can imagine that the job of the invoicing clerk would be made very efficient if, when he or she keys in the customer code number, the code number of a product purchased, and the quantity, the computer automatically displays both the customer details and the product details, and updates both the customer file and the product file with the relevant details of the transaction.

That is exactly what a relational database does – it links files together, so that information from both can be displayed or printed, and enabling both to be updated.

Often, more than two files will be linked in this way. In the above sales situation, for instance, there may be three files:

- An order file containing details of the order (the customer's code number, the product code numbers and quantities, and the date), from which the total order value is calculated and invoices and delivery notes produced.
- A customer file containing the customer's name and address, together with the value of orders and their dates, from which the monthly statement is produced.
- A product file containing the product details such as quantities received and issued, and from which purchase orders are produced to send to suppliers.

The order file picks up the customer details from the customer file, and the product details from the product file. It in turn updates the customer file with the value of the order, and the product file with the number of issues.

This is a simplified description of what actually goes on in a sales accounting situation, but it illustrates the value of relational databases.

## 6.8    Client/server database architecture

In some of the more advanced database systems, the task of data storage is separated from the task of processing the data. The former is carried out by *server* software, while the latter is carried out by the *client* package. The server software normally resides in a mainframe of minicomputer, or perhaps on a network server, and it handles basic data storage tasks. The client can be any database package that is able to accept data from the server; it provides the user interface as well as the various input and output facilities. Other kinds of application package, such as spreadsheets, can also act as clients. The server software is also referred to as the *back-end*, and the application software is referred to as the *front-end*.

In recent years *Structured Query Language* (SQL) has become important. This is a database language that allows clients to communicate with servers. The client sends instructions to the server in this language, one example being the instruction to find all records that match certain criteria. Normally, the user can simply select a menu choice offered by the client, and the software generates the necessary instructions. Often, the client package will also allow the user to type the commands directly, should he so wish. The data will be retrieved by the server, passed to the client, and will appear at the right place in the application (which might be a spreadsheet or word processed document) as though it had been typed in.

A number of (client) application packages now support SQL and can therefore make use of server software. They include Paradox and DataEase. SQL is also available for Excel, Microsoft's spreadsheet package. Two well-known and powerful SQL servers are Oracle and Ingres.

### 6.9   Record-keeping concepts

Let's turn now to the main record-keeping concepts. These are *data*, *file*, *record*, *field*, and *template*.

*Data.*   The purpose of record keeping is to store, retrieve, and analyse data on a variety of topics. Some data are numbers, examples being ages of people, prices of goods, and quantities. Other data, however, are alphabetic or alphanumeric information, examples being names and postcodes.

*File.*   A record-keeping package enables you to set up files to store data on a variety of topics. For example, you might keep one file containing names and addresses, another containing details of customers' orders, and another containing details of stock held in your department. Not only does the type of data differ from file to file, but the way in which it is organized, or structured, differs also. On personal computer systems, a file (of records) is simply another word for database.

*Record.*   A record is a single unit of structured data in a file. In a name-and-address file, for example, a record is the data relating to one individual, organized in the following way:

the name
several lines of address
the telephone number.

All the records in a file have an identical structure. That structure serves the same purpose as the printed design on the cards in a card index. The data varies from record to record, but the structure remains the same.

*Field.*   A field is the space in a record occupied by a single item of data, such as a name, or a line of an address, or a price, or a quantity. The set of fields, and the spaces allocated to them, determine the structure of a record.

*Key.*   One of the fields in a record may be a *key field*, meaning that the data in this field uniquely identifies the record and distinguishes it from all other records in the file. Often, it is this field that will be used when the computer searches for a specific record. In many cases, a code number will be the key; in the case of an employee record, for example, a works number or personnel number will be the key.

*Template.*   A template is the structure of a file without the data. When you create a file, your first task is to design the template. It's a bit like designing the printing that is to go on the cards in a card index. You decide the fields you need, their position, the space to be allocated to each, and any labels (names) that you are going to give them. In the case of a computer-based system, you can build other things into your design, such as automatic date-stamping when a record is added to a file, automatic calculation of balances and totals of numeric fields, and automatic checks on the validity (i.e. reasonableness) of the data when it is entered.

Figure 6.2 shows a demonstration template for a student record system. (A real-life template would be bigger, with

STUDENT RECORDS

| SUBJECT | 1 | 2 | 3 | 4 | 5 | 6 | 7 | 8 | 9 | 10 | AVG | EXAM |
|---|---|---|---|---|---|---|---|---|---|---|---|---|
| English | | | | | | | | | | | | |
| Mathematics | | | | | | | | | | | | |
| Gen. Studies | | | | | | | | | | | | |

Surname:   Forename:   DOB:
Street:   Town:   County:
Postcode:   Phone:

Dept:   Course:   Year:   Tutor:

Comments   Overall average

*Figure 6.2*   Template for a student records file

more subjects.) There are fields, and field labels, to record the name, address, and other personal details of each student, more fields in the boxes in the lower half of the template to enter assignment and exam grades for the various subjects, and a final field at the bottom for the tutor's comments. In this template, the student's average grades are automatically recalculated whenever assignment grades are added to his record; Q&A, the software package used to create this file, allows the template to be programmed so that this sort of feature is easily built it. The computer displays this template on the screen whenever a record is added to the student record file, allowing you to add data into each field. When you retrieve the record later on, the template is again displayed, together with that record's data.

## 6.10   Record-keeping tasks

The tasks that need to be carried out on a database file are as follows.

*Designing the file.*   Before you can keep records, you must first design the template and other parts of the record-keeping system. It's worth taking some trouble over this task, as you only have to carry it out once. Templates designed for one file can often be used for others, though perhaps with some modification.

*Adding and deleting records.*   Once the template has been designed you can start adding records to your file. From time to time you will need to add more new records, and you will need to delete from the file old records that are no longer required. In the case of the student records file, for example, many new records have to be added at the start of each year, and the records of students who have left deleted.

*Updating records.*   You need to keep records up to date by entering new data in them. For example, you need to enter stock movements in the case of a stock file, or assignment grades in the case of student records. You may also need to amend data which is no longer correct, as when the price of a stock item changes, or a student moves to a new address.

*Validating data.*   Because of the risk of human error, you need to build into your system automatic checks on the validity, or reasonableness, of the data that you enter. This may mean checking that it lies within a certain range, or that it is of the right type, e.g. textual, or numerical.

*Searching records.*   You need to be able to locate individual records, perhaps to deal with queries. For example, you may need to look up the record of a student to check his or her performance; or to look up a particular stock item to check the balance in stock. You also need to be able to find all records that conform to certain criteria. For example, you may want to find all students who achieved less than a certain mark in English, or all stock items with stock balances below the reorder level.

*Sorting records.*   You may also wish to sort the records in a file into order. For example, you may want to list student records alphabetically by name, or in order of overall grade.

*Calculating.*   There are a variety of calculations you may wish to carry out on the records in a file. You may wish to update stock balances each time there is a stock movement, or calculate the total value of all stock held.

*Reporting.*   You will also need to produce periodic reports which summarize the data held in a file. In the case of the student records, for example, you may want to know the average marks achieved by the class for each assignment, in order to check out the effectiveness of the teaching and assignment program. In the case of the stock records, you may want to produce reorder lists of stock that is running out, or a summary of stock movements by category of stock.

## 6.11 Database applications

Databases are useful at both the managerial and clerical levels in an organization. At the managerial level they are a decision-support tool, for reports can be produced from them which summarize what's going on and give pointers for the future. At the clerical level they provide an easy way of entering and retrieving data, and dealing with enquiries.

So in many situations a clerk will require access to a database to carry out the latter type of task, and a manager will require access to it to get out a report. Where personal computers are used, this may mean two or three people having access to the same PC, or else setting up a configuration of multiuser or networked PCs.

Some database applications are almost exclusively 'clerical', an example being a name-and-address file. Most database applications, though, have both clerical and managerial elements.

Typical business database applications include:

- Stock records.
- Personnel records.
- Customer records.
- Accounts.
- Mailing lists.

## 6.12 Spreadsheet software

A spreadsheet is a software package which organizes data in the form of a table or *worksheet*. An example of a worksheet is shown in Figure 6.3. This is a simple cash-flow forecast for a small business. As you can see from this example, it is mainly with numbers, and calculations on numbers, that spreadsheets are concerned.

In this worksheet, if you alter any of the income or expenditure data, the computer immediately and automatically recalculates the cash-flow forecast on the bottom lines.

|   | A | B | C | D | E | F | G | H |
|---|---|---|---|---|---|---|---|---|
| 1 |  | Cash-flow forecast for Pine Workshop, Jan-June 1988 | | | | | | |
| 2 |  |  |  |  |  |  |  |  |
| 3 |  |  | JAN | FEB | MAR | APR | MAY | JUN |
| 4 | INCOME | ======================================================= | | | | | | |
| 5 | Sales |  | 9500 | 10000 | 10500 | 11000 | 11000 | 11500 |
| 6 | Other |  | 2000 | 1000 | 1500 | 1300 | 1500 | 1500 |
| 7 |  | ------------------------------------------------------- | | | | | | |
| 8 | Total |  | 11500 | 11000 | 12000 | 12300 | 12500 | 13000 |
| 9 | EXPENSES | ======================================================= | | | | | | |
| 10 | Wages |  | 3300 | 3500 | 3700 | 4000 | 4000 | 4200 |
| 11 | Stock |  | 3000 | 3000 | 3000 | 3300 | 3300 | 3500 |
| 12 | Rent |  | 1200 | 1200 | 1200 | 1200 | 1200 | 1200 |
| 13 | Rates |  | 400 | 400 | 400 | 400 | 400 | 400 |
| 14 | Fuel |  | 350 | 350 | 350 | 300 | 300 | 300 |
| 15 | Other |  | 1000 | 1000 | 1200 | 1200 | 1200 | 1200 |
| 16 |  | ------------------------------------------------------- | | | | | | |
| 17 | Total |  | 9250 | 9450 | 9850 | 10400 | 10400 | 10800 |
| 18 |  | ======================================================= | | | | | | |
| 19 | B/F |  | 10000 | 12250 | 13800 | 15950 | 17850 | 19950 |
| 20 | BALANCE |  | 12250 | 13800 | 15950 | 17850 | 19950 | 22150 |

*Figure 6.3*   Cash-flow forecast worksheet

As anyone who has had anything to do with cash-flow forecasts will testify, this is much better than having to do the job manually.

Spreadsheets have some similarities with the record-keeping packages described in the last chapter, and you can think of a worksheet as a file of records listed in tabular form:

- Each column in a worksheet corresponds to a field in a record.
- Each row corresponds to a record.
- Programming statements can be inserted so that calculations are carried out automatically.

(You can, in fact, import a set of records prepared on a database package such as Q&A into a spreadsheet package such as Lotus 1-2-3. When you do so, the records will be listed in worksheet form. Or you can import a Lotus worksheet into a database package such as Q&A, and each row becomes a separate record.)

## 6.13    Spreadsheet concepts

Spreadsheets share a number of concepts with record-keeping packages, including the concepts of *file*, *data*, *label*, and *template*. Concepts that are special to spreadsheets, which are dealt with below, are *column*, *row*, *cell*, *formula*, and *window*.

*Column.* A worksheet is split vertically into columns, which can correspond to the fields in a database. The default column width is normally 9 characters, though this can easily be altered either globally (i.e. across the entire worksheet) or for individual columns. Most spreadsheet packages will cope with worksheets running into hundreds of columns, though the number you can actually use depends upon the amount of RAM in your computer.

Columns are normally identified by letters, starting A, B, C, . . . , and continuing through AA, AB, AC, . . . , BA, BB, BC, and so on. To make the worksheets you design easy to read, you should label each column by typing a heading at the top. In Figure 6.3, the column labels are the months of the year.

*Row.* A worksheet is also split into rows, i.e. horizontal lines of data which can correspond to the records in a database. Rows are numbered downwards, starting at 1. Most spreadsheet packages will, in theory, permit worksheets extending to several thousand rows, though in practice the number you can use depends on your computer's RAM. To make your worksheet design easy to read, you should normally type in row labels at the left, as is done in Figure 6.3.

*Cell.* A cell is the space occupied by an individual item of data in a worksheet. It is identified by the column letter and row number in which it lies. For example, the cell lying at the intersection of column C and row 4 is called C4.

*Formula.* Besides data, a cell can contain a programming statement, or *formula*. These are not visible when you are entering data, but they reside in the background. A formula normally involves a mathematical calculation on the contents of other cells, the result being inserted in the cell which contains it.

*Window.* Most business worksheets are quite large,

extending beyond the edges of the computer screen. The screen is, in effect, a 'window' into the worksheet. Many spreadsheet packages allow you to set up two or more windows onto your worksheet, so that two or more parts of it can be displayed at the same time on the screen.

## 6.14   Moving around the worksheet

You move the cursor from cell to cell within the spreadsheet window using the arrow keys; when the cursor reaches the edge of the window, any further movement forces the worksheet to scroll past the window. Bigger jumps through the worksheet are possible by using other keys, e.g. by pressing the PgUp or PgDn keys to jump a 'page' (i.e. window) up or down, or by pressing the CTRL key and an arrow key.

## 6.15   Spreadsheet tasks

To set up and use a worksheet, you have to carry out the following tasks.

*Designing the worksheet.*   First, you have to design the template. This is a bit like setting up a template for a record-keeping system. You have to:

- Decide how the data is to be organized.
- Insert appropriate column and row labels.
- Adjust the column widths as necessary.
- Set the number of decimal places for displaying the data.
- Program the template, i.e. enter programming statements and formulae in appropriate cells.

As with a record-keeping system, this is a once-only job, and templates set up for one application can often be used for others, though perhaps with some modification. Public domain templates are available for the most popular spreadsheet packages, and by using these you can set up many standard applications with the minimum of effort. For most spreadsheet applications it's not too difficult to do the job yourself from scratch.

*Adding data.* Once the template has been designed, you can enter the data for your application. Any results (totals, averages, etc.) will be automatically calculated, using the formulae stored in the results cells.

*Altering data.* You will often wish to alter numbers previously entered into a cell. For example, if you are using a cash-flow forecast worksheet like that shown in Figure 6.3, you may wish to find out how changes in certain costs, or sales, affect your future cash flows. You have merely to enter the new figures, and the computer instantly calculates the results. This kind of activity is very useful for decision-making and planning, because you can easily and quickly investigate the effects of alternative courses of action.

*Goal-seeking.* Sometimes, you may have certain ideal results which you wish to achieve. You could keep altering the data in your worksheet until what you want is produced in the results cell. Many spreadsheet packages, however, incorporate automatic goal-seeking: you say what you want the results to be, and the spreadsheet will work backwards to the starting data.

*Charting.* Most spreadsheet packages will produce various kinds of charts and graphs of the data in the worksheet. Normally, column labels will be used to mark the X-axis, with a selection of data or results being plotted against the Y-axis.

*Sorting and searching.* Many spreadsheet packages provide limited database facilities such as sorting rows, e.g. into alphabetical order or row labels, or searching for a particular entry.

## 6.16 Spreadsheets and databases compared

Some tasks can be carried out using either a spreadsheet or a database package. For example, you could keep your personal accounts on either. However, there are important differences in the two types of package:

- Database packages have sophisticated data retrieval and reporting facilities which are not normally found in spreadsheets.

- A spreadsheet provides a more flexible working environment, for it is not limited to the kind of record structures described in the last chapter; for example, a row does not have to be a 'record', but can be programmed to show totals, averages, or other results.

So when should you use a spreadsheet, and when a database? Spreadsheets are particularly good for handling numerical data and calculating results, and so they are appropriate for many financial and other numerical/calculating applications. Database packages are more appropriate for conventional record-keeping tasks where the main requirement is to retrieve information and produce transaction documents and reports.

## 6.17    Spreadsheet applications

Spreadsheet applications fall into two broad areas, managerial and clerical:

- Managerial applications are those that support the kinds of task that managers have to carry out, in particular decision-making and planning tasks. As mentioned above, spreadsheets enable you easily and quickly to investigate the effects of alternative courses of action. Cash-flow forecasting is a favourite managerial application, and others include profit forecasting, investment appraisal, manpower planning, and statistical analyses.
- Clerical applications are those that support bookkeeping and other office tasks that are normally carried out by clerks.

## 6.18    Word processing and desktop publishing

Word processing (WP) software aims to make the task of creating and editing text as easy and powerful as possible. In the past, WP packages did not allow you to use a variety of fonts (typestyles) or to incorporate graphics in your documents. Desktop publishing (DTP) software, in contrast, provides very weak word processing facilities, for it assumes that you will create your text using a WP package, but it does allow you to use a wide range of fonts, to control exactly the layout of your material on the page, and to include graphics.

In recent years, however, this distinction between WP and DTP has become less pronounced. Most modern WP packages now allow you to use a variety of fonts, and some will allow you to incorporate graphics in your documents. At the same time, DTP packages are improving their WP features. Nevertheless, at the time of writing the two types of software are quite different, and it is still appropriate to deal with them separately.

I'll deal with WP software in this chapter. DTP software, which is part of the graphics and multimedia revolution in computing, is covered in the next chapter.

## 6.19   Word processing concepts

The main WP concepts are *outline, edit, window, text enhancement, WYSIWYG, page definition, style sheet, block operation, glossary,* and *mailmerge*.

*Outline.* An outline is the skeleton structure of a document, often just a list of headings, subheadings, and sub-subheadings. Outlining software exists which enables you to draw up such a list, and then juggle the items around at will and add notes, a sort of 'ideas organizer'. Once you have outlined your document, you can start to fill in the text under the headings and subheadings. Some word processors incorporate outlining facilities, allowing you to 'collapse' text under headings, so that it disappears from view on the screen. You can then see the structure of your document more clearly, and shuffle headings (with the hidden text) around if you wish to change the order. I'll be saying more on this on page 146.

*Edit.* *Editing* refers to the process of entering and amending text. Because this takes place electronically, avoiding the need to laboriously correct documents or retype pages, word processing has revolutionized the writing process.

*Window.* As with spreadsheets, the screen is a window into the document you are editing. You can move around the window using the arrow keys, larger jumps being possible by pressing, for example, the CTRL key and an arrow key. When the cursor reaches the edge of the screen, further movements cause the document to scroll. Some WP software allows you to create two or more windows on the screen, so that you see two parts of a document at the same time, or view two different documents. You can then easily copy or move text between the two parts of the document.

*Text enhancement.*   This refers to special effects such as embolding or underlining, or selecting special fonts. You enhance individual characters or words in your document by positioning the cursor on them and pressing either a function key or the ALT key and a character key – the process varies from package to package. Some WP packages show these effects on the screen exactly as they will appear on paper, so that italics, for example, actually look that way. Other packages are only able to highlight or colour the characters that have been enhanced. How these effects will actually come out on paper depends on the printer you are using.

*WYSIWYG.*   This stands for 'What You See Is What You Get'. In other words, what's on the screen shows what the document will look like when printed. Most WP packages are WYSIWYG so far as the organization of the text is concerned: they show where lines end, the spaces between paragraphs, where the page breaks are, and so on. However, few are WYSIWYG to the extent that they show both this and how the various text enhancements will look.

*Page definition.*   This refers to the line length, margin size, number of lines per page, and other page formatting that you have set up for your document. WYSIWYG word processors show on the screen how the page definition affects the appearance of the document. When you create a new document, your WP package will provide a default page definition, with the line lengths etc. set up already. If you want your document formatted differently, you can easily change the settings. Many packages also allow you to decide the defaults, so that most of your documents are automatically formatted the way you want them.

*Style sheet.*   Besides the overall page definition, some word processors enable you to set other aspects of layout style, such as indenting the first line of paragraphs. You can prepare a variety of page definitions and styles for different types of document, and save these as *style sheets*. Then, when you create a document, you can attach the appropriate style sheet to it so that the pre-defined page definition style is automatically applied, and paragraph styles are available for applying to individual paragraphs.

*Block operation.* This refers to the process of deleting, moving, copying, or enhancing a complete block of text, such as several sentences or paragraphs. The process involves marking the start and the end of the block in some way, then pressing a special key.

*Glossary.* Many organizations often use identical paragraphs or other sections of text time and time again in many documents. An obvious example is a solicitor's office, producing legal documents for house conveyancing and other transactions. It makes sense to store all these sections of text on disk and insert them as required in documents. Such stored paragraphs and sections of text are called *glossaries*, and some word processors incorporate a special facility to handle them.

*Mailmerge.* This refers to the process of merging a document with data in a database, in order to print a number of personalized letters. A typical application is inserting automatically in a standard letter the names and addresses of people on a mailing list.

## 6.20   Word processing tasks

Producing a document using a word processing package involves a number of possible operations. Here's a comprehensive list; often you won't use them all.

*Outlining your document.* If you are creating a long and complex document, such as a report, it is helpful to produce an outline of it first. I find drawing up an outline on paper a tedious and untidy process, as I keep wanting to make changes. The best way is to use outlining software on the computer, an excellent public domain (shareware) package for the PC being PC-Outline. GrandView, the package I normally use for word processing, is primarily an outliner which includes the standard range of word processing facilities.

*Creating your document.*   Once your outline is complete,
you can start word processing your document. In theory,
you could write the sections of your document in any order,
selecting outline headings to work on at will. In practice,
most people find it best to start at the beginning and work
through to the end, perhaps adding ideas under outline
headings as they come to mind. As you create your masterpiece your ideas will mature and your emphases alter, and
you will want to modify the outline somewhat; this becomes
difficult to do if you start by creating sections lying in the
middle of your document.

As mentioned already, when you start a new document
your word processor will provide you with a default page
definition (line length etc.). If you wish to alter this page
definition for the current document, you can do so at any
time.

*Editing your document.*   As you work on your document,
you will want to make changes, and word processing packages provide many powerful tools to help with this. These
tools include the following:

- Easy *deleting* facilities, so that you can quickly move to
  the offending section of text, and delete it character by
  character, or word by word, or by marking the whole
  block for deletion.
- *Undo* facilities, so that you can restore text that you
  have deleted in error. You can also use this facility to
  move text: you delete the text, move the cursor to the
  spot where you want it put, and press the undo key.
- *Moving* and *copying* facilities, to move or copy blocks
  of text within your documents.
- *Merge* facilities, to incorporate standard paragraphs,
  addresses, and other textual material stored on disk into
  your document. The process of compiling a document
  by merging a number of existing pieces of text is called
  *boilerplating*.
- *Search and replace* facilities, which will automatically
  search for a word (or words, or part of a word), and, if
  required, replace it by another. You can ask the computer to automatically replace the word 'globally', i.e.
  throughout the document, or you can check each occur-
  rence of the word before allowing it to be replaced.

- *Spelling check* facilities, using an electronic dictionary stored on disk, which enables you to check the spelling of an individual word (which you select by moving the cursor to it), or all words throughout the document. If a word does not match what's in the dictionary, the computer highlights it and displays a list of possible replacements on the screen. Most spelling checkers allow you to add additional words to this dictionary, a facility which is particularly useful if you write technical reports or other material with unusual words.
- Some word processors also provide an electronic *thesaurus*, which will, on request, display a list of words with a meaning similar to the word lying at the cursor. This may help you to improve your style by replacing complex words by simpler or more appropriate ones, or by adding more variety to your choice of words.
- *Word count* facilities, so that as you work on your document you can check whether the length is on target, and make cuts or add more material if it is not.

*Checking your style.* When you have finished your document, you can, if you wish, test its readability using style-checking software. This will perform a number of tests, such as:

- Determining the complexity of your sentence structure, by calculating the average number of words and the average number of clauses per sentence.
- Determining the complexity of the words used, by calculating the percentage of words with three or more syllables.
- Checking the amount of jargon in your text.
- Checking the amount of variety in your text.
- Comparing impersonal words like 'its' and 'their' to personal words like 'your' and 'yours' to determine the personal tone of the text.

When it has checked the document, the software will produce a report giving a readability index, a jargon index, sentence structure recommendations, and so on. The most lucid style will normally rate a reading age of around 14, with an average sentence length of 18 to 20 words. Some style-checking software will also provide detailed comments on individual sentences, such as those that are too long.

*Printing your document.* Once you have got your document the way you want it, you will want to print it. Word processors generally provide a number of print options, including:

- A choice of line spacing options.
- The ability to *right-justify* the text (i.e. line up the right-hand edges of lines as is done in this book) by inserting extra spaces between words.
- The ability to insert *headers* at the top or *footers* at the bottom of each page (such as the chapter name) and to number the pages.
- The ability to print the text in two or more columns down the page.

*Producing mailmerged documents.* Most WP packages provide mailmerge facilities, so that data from a database can be incorporated in a document when it is printed. With Q&A, a package I've mentioned already, all you do is enter the field labels in your document, distinguishing them from the rest of your text by enclosing them between asterisks. When you print the document, you specify the name of the database file, and which records from the file are to be used. Q&A then prints repeated copies of the letter, one for each record, with the data from that record entered in place of the asterisked field names.

*Importing and exporting files.* You may wish to include in your document material produced on other packages. Most software provides facilities to export data or text produced in them, i.e. to save the data or text in files that conform to a universally-recognized format. Such formats include ASCII for text, DIF (Document Interchange Format) for data, as well as the dBase and Lotus 1-2-3 formats. Once in that standard format, the files can be imported into other software. When a word processed document is exported as an ASCII file, all the special characters that produce text enhancements and other formatting are stripped out, leaving the bare text.

## 6.21 WP applications

Word processing has a large number of applications, and these are increasing all the time as the power of WP packages improves and starts to incorporate DTP capabilities. The obvious applications are:

- Notes.
- Letters.
- Memos.
- Reports.
- Articles and books.

## 6.22 Personal productivity software

Personal productivity software helps you organize and execute your own work. It replaces the diaries, calendars, calculators, notepads, and other desktop accessories used by office workers, and so it is sometimes referred to as *desktop accessory software.*

Some personal productivity software, such as Homebase (described earlier in this chapter), or Sidekick Plus, or PC Tools, aims to encompass all or most of these desktop accessories within a single package. Often, this software is RAM-resident, meaning that it remains in the computer's memory while you are running another application, ready to spring to life on the screen at the touch of a key.

To illustrate the value of Sidekick Plus and similar RAM-resident products, suppose you are using an application (such as a database, spreadsheet, or word processor), and you need to do something such as looking up a phone number, making a diary entry, or performing a calculation. You don't have to quit your application in order to run your desk accessory software, instead you press the key that calls up the desk accessory onto the screen, look up the information or make the entry, then press another key to return to your application at the point where you left it. This kind of facility has obvious benefits for the office worker, making the computer a very flexible information–handling device.

## 6.23  Ideas organizers

An ideas organizer, or 'outliner' as it is normally called, is software that enables you to organize entries – which might be tasks, topics, names, or other textual information – into a hierarchical list of headlines. Sidekick Plus includes an outlining module, and PC-Outline and GrandView are excellent outliners which can also be used in RAM-resident mode.

I produced the outline of this book using GrandView (which is not only an excellent outliner but also a first-class word processor). The chapter titles were the main headlines; major topics within chapters were subheadlines, which were broken down into more detailed sub-subheadlines. The computer allows you to easily shuffle the headlines around, promote subheadlines to higher levels or demote headlines to lower levels, divide headlines in two or combine separate headlines into one, very quickly and easily.

Most outliners also allow you to collapse (i.e. hide) low-level headlines, so that you can get an instant overview of your main headlines, and immediately expand them again when you want a more detailed view. You can insert text below any headline, which might be a few notes or a substantial document. You can collapse this text, so that it does not get in the way of the rest of the outline, and you can instantly expand it again.

Many outliners allow you to use a variety of labelling styles. For example, major headlines could be labelled I, II, III, etc., subheadlines could be labelled, A, B, C, etc., sub-subheadlines could be labelled 1, 2, 3, . . ., and so on. Or you could, if you wished, have no labels at all.

The kinds of tasks you can use outliners for are:

- Developing the outline of a report or a task. You can enter major headlines, then break these down into subheadlines, insert additional headlines or subheadlines at any time, and easily rearrange the outline until you have marshalled your thoughts into order.
- Keeping a file of names, addresses, and telephone numbers. In this file, individual names might be the main headlines, with the addresses and phone numbers forming subsidiary text. Normally, you will collapse this

text, so that only a list of names is visible. New names and addresses can be added at any time, the list can be sorted into alphabetical order (using the outliner's sort facility), and individual names can be quickly located using the search facility.

- Maintaining a 'to-do' list for tasks that are not tied to a particular time and so do not fit into your diary. For this application you will probably have two main headlines, namely 'To do' and 'Done'. New tasks are added under the first headline, and tasks which have been completed are moved from the first headline to the second.

## 6.24    Expert systems

An expert system is a sophisticated type of application package which:

- Stores a large number of facts and rules about a field of knowledge, or *domain*.
- Provides way of linking these facts and rules so that guidance can be given on questions that might be asked within that domain.

Put simply, it is a way of recording and accessing human knowledge in a particular domain. Expert systems have been developed for several domains, including medicine, geology, chemistry, mathematics, and various aspects of business, including repair and maintenance.

To construct an expert system, people who are experts in the domain are interviewed at terminals and their knowledge of the domain – i.e. of the facts and rules contained in it – is keyed in, using a logic programming language. Examples of simple facts and rules written in one such language (PROLOG) are given in Chapter 4. To make use of the knowledge stored in the system, it is necessary to ask questions in the format required by the language or system.

A language like PROLOG is difficult for inexperienced people to use, and so a front-end or 'shell' is normally provided. This is a type of application software running in the logic programming language. It is used both by experts in the domain to set up the knowledge base and to keep it up to date, and by users wishing to interrogate it.

One example of an expert system is MYCIN, which is used for the diagnosis and treatment of bacterial infections. To set it up, a number of consultants invested thousands of hours of work in building up the knowledge base. A typical rule contained in that base is:

| | |
|---|---|
| IF | The infection is primary-bacteremia |
| AND | The site of the culture is one of the sterile sites |
| AND | The suspected portal of entry is the gastro-intestinal tract |
| THEN | There is suggestive evidence (0.7 probability) that the identity of the organism is bacteriodes. |

Having been set up, MYCIN supports doctors and medical assistants who lack specialist bacteriological knowledge and who would otherwise have to call upon the help of a consultant. One obvious benefit of this is that proper medical care can be given in situations where consultants are not available. Another more surprising benefit is that, even in situations where consultants are available, MYCIN can actually give better advice. The reason for this is that it contains the knowledge of a number of consultants, not just one, and so is able to draw on a broad base of knowledge and expertise.

When consulted, MYCIN asks the doctor or medical assistant a number of questions about the patient in order to establish the facts of the case. Examples of such facts are the first three lines of the above rule. To answer the questions, the enquirer may have to carry out certain tests on the patient. When the system has elicited sufficient facts, it draws conclusions based on the rules stored in its knowledge base, and assigns probabilities to those conclusions. In the example above, the assigned probability is 0.7, i.e. 70%

An expert system consists of three components:

- A *knowledge base*, containing the facts and rules gleaned from human experts about a particular domain.
- A *knowledge manager*, i.e. a piece of software which controls the knowledge base. This allows the user to update the base with new knowledge received from

experts, and to make inferences from the existing knowledge in order to answer questions. An important part of the knowledge manager's task is to give explanations, when asked, of the reasoning behind the conclusions it draws.

- A *situation model*, containing data on the current situation or case. This is used by the knowledge manager to retrieve the appropriate information from the knowledge base.

Conclusions drawn by the knowledge manager which have proved useful can be 'remembered', i.e. stored in the knowledge base. In this way the system can learn with use, and so become more expert. Being independent of the knowledge base, the knowledge manager created for one expert system can be used for other related systems. For example, the MYCIN knowledge manager is used in the EMYCIN system, which is a medical expert system designed for handling a number of different knowledge bases.

## 6.25   Expert systems for business

The first business applications to be computerized were payroll and invoicing, the reason being that they are governed by unambiguous rules, procedures, and facts. Later, other more complex applications were computerized, but they, too, had to be reduced to precisely defined rules and facts in a program. Expert systems are no different – they are most easily applied in situations where the rules and facts are unambiguous and where conclusions can be logically drawn and assigned probabilities.

So expert systems applications in business are those which can most easily be reduced to rules. Typical applications are:

- Social security regulations in the DHSS, to allow people to obtain advice on their entitlements.
- Income tax regulations, so that advice can be given on ways to minimize tax liability.
- Maintenance and repair work, where the steps required to track down faults can be precisely defined for each type of equipment.

Expert systems are not widely used in the office at present, though there is no shortage of possible applications. These include office procedures, company regulations, and personnel management.

One expert system for the Apple Macintosh is Sales Edge, a product of Human Edge Software Corporation. This can be used to analyse the personality factors of the parties involved in a transaction (the seller and the buyer), from which it advises the salesman on the strategy to adopt. When the salesman runs the program, he is asked to agree or disagree with a number of statements about himself, and then to agree or disagree with a number of adjectives that describe the buyer. When this has been done, the program produces a sales strategy in the form of a report several pages long.

## 6.26   Project planning

Complex projects, such as publishing a magazine, installing a large computer system, or conducting a market survey, require a considerable amount of planning and control. Not only are they made up of many stages, but they involve considerable expenditure on resources of people, plant, equipment, etc. Project planning techniques to aid this task were developed in the 1960s, and in recent years these techniques have been implemented on personal computers.

In essence, project planning involves breaking down a large project into manageable stages or *activities*, and deciding for each when it should start, what resources it needs, and how long it should take with these resources. The object is to complete the project on time and within the budgeted costs.

Some activities are critical to the project time – if they are delayed, they will hold up other activities, which will have repercussions through the rest of the project and affect the overall project time. Other activities are not critical, and these can suffer some delay without affecting other activities and without therefore delaying the rest of the project. The amount by which a non-critical activity can be delayed is called its *float*.

An important part of project planning is to isolate the

critical activities, so that attention and resources can be concentrated on them to ensure that no delays to the overall project time occur. The sequence of critical activities is called the *critical path*. Project planning software will automatically isolate the critical path and compute the overall project time and the amount of float available for each non-critical activity.

To use a project planning package, you must:

- Break down the project into activities, and estimate for each the resources required and its duration.
- Determine dependencies, i.e. which activities depend upon the prior completion of earlier activities.
- Key this information into the computer.

The computer will then, under the control of the project planning software, carry out the necessary calculations, and will often display the result in the form of a special sort of bar chart called a Gantt chart. Each bar of the chart represents an activity, with shading to indicate slack time (if any), and with the critical activities highlighted.

During the course of the project, the data in the computer is kept up-to-date by keying in the date when each activity is completed. If there has been slippage, so that an actual completion date differs from the projected date, the effect on the critical path is computed, as well as the new project time. Some activities which previously were not critical may now be critical, and if this is the case the computer updates the critical path. This helps management control the project, by highlighting the effects of slippage and indicating the critical activities to watch.

# 7
# Graphics and multimedia

## 7.1 Graphics

The use of computers for graphics applications is a relatively recent phenomenon, as it requires suitable monitors and printers to output the results. The computer graphics revolution was to a large extent created by the Apple Mac in the mid 1980s, with its graphics-oriented operating system, its high-resolution monitor, and its marriage to the low-cost laser printers that had started to appear. The PC-compatible world is only now, at the start of the 1990s, catching up.

So far as 'the office' is concerned, computer graphics can be considered to embrace the following applications:

- *Drawing*. Creating designs using the computer's facilities.
- *Charting and graphing*. Creating bar charts, graphs, etc. of numerical data, as well as wordcharts for textual data.
- *Presentations*. Displaying drawings and charts as a 'slide show'.
- *Desktop publishing*. Bringing together text and graphics for outputting to a high-quality printer.

Often, a number of these applications will be combined in a single package. For example, the two main presentation packages for the PC, Lotus Freelance and Harvard Graphics, include sophisticated drawing, charting, and graphing features. With these packages you can, for example, create a graph of some numerical data, enhance it with suitable drawings and text, then present it as part of a computer slide show. Also available for the PC is the GEM Presentation Team, which includes the GEM Draw, GEM Word chart, and GEM Graph packages. There are also some very powerful dedicated drawing packages such as CorelDraw.

Computer graphics applications include animation and 'painting' software. These are not only relevant for the entertainment world, they are also used in the office for, for example, sales and other presentations.

Two general comments about this software which are worth making are:

1   They all make extensive use of the mouse, as this is a much better device for painting and drawing on the screen than the keyboard.
2   A variety of methods for presenting the computer images produced by this software are available. For example, laser printers can produce excellent printouts on ordinary paper or on transparencies for overhead projectors. Also, the screen image can be photographed using a special camera to produce 35 mm slides. More sophisticated film recorders will convert the computer graphics file directly into a slide, which overcomes the fuzziness caused by the relatively low resolution of the screen. Another alternative is to connect either a large screen display monitor to the computer, or a special display which sits on top of an overhead projector and throws a large image onto a white screen.

In the first part of this chapter I shall deal with the applications listed above. In the second part, I shall deal with the marriage of the computer with other media technologies such as audio and video.

## 7.2   Painting software

With painting software, you can draw freehand pictures on the computer screen, using lines of varying widths and colours, and fill in (or 'paint') areas of the drawing with colours and patterns. A variety of painting 'tools' are provided by this software, and you select these by pointing with the mouse at the appropriate icon displayed in an on-screen 'toolbox'. You can select colours and patterns in a similar way from an on-screen palette.

Figure 7.1 is the screen display from GEM Paint, showing a painting, the toolbox, and the palette. The painting tools include:

- A *pencil* to draw lines.
- A *spraycan* to create air-brush effects.
- An *eraser* to rub out.
- A *microscope* to zoom in on part of the picture in order to make very detailed and precise changes.

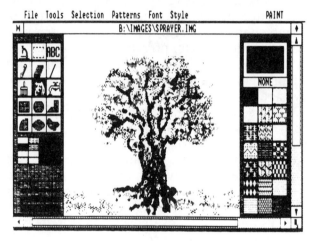

*Figure 7.1*   A GEM Paint display

Clip-art libraries are also available for many painting programs. These consist of collections of drawings and artwork, produced on the computer by professional artists and designers, which can be freely added to your own pictures. They include images of people, office equipment, buildings, etc. You can also add small amounts of text to your picture.

## 7.3   Drawing software

This software provides the electronic equivalent of a set of mathematical drawing tools – a pen to draw with, a ruler compasses, set-square, etc. With it, you can draw accurate designs of, for example, buildings and simple manufactured objects. Unlike painting packages, this software is no primarily intended for freehand drawing, instead providing an easy way of drawing straight lines or lines that follow a mathematical curve (such as a circle).

Although quite inadequate for professional draftsmen or architects, drawing software includes several tools found in the more sophisticated computer-aided design packages:

- *Gridlock*, to ensure that the ends of lines are accurately positioned according to a predefined grid of points.
- *Copy*, to reproduce an already-drawn object at other positions in the drawing. So if you are designing an office layout, for example, you can draw one desk and then copy it to a number of locations.
- *Move*, allowing you to reposition an already-drawn object.
- *Delete*, enabling you to remove lines or objects from your drawing.

You can also include a number of standard mathematical objects in your drawing, such as rectangles and circles, and you can add small amounts of text (e.g. captions) to your drawings (see Figure 7.2).

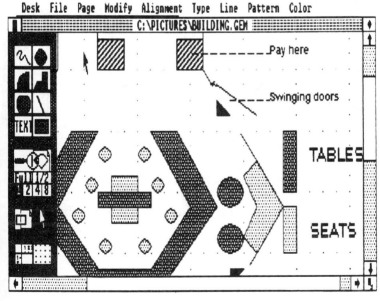

*Figure 7.2*   A GEM Draw display

## 7.4    Wordchart software

Wordchart software enables you to quickly design notices, overhead transparencies, and other single-sheet textual displays. You might think that word processing software would be suitable for this task; however, as explained below, wordcharting software makes the job much easier, and, for the ordinary user, gives a much better result.

GEM Wordchart (Figure 7.3) is particularly good. With it, notices and other textual displays can generally be broken down into several zones. Typically, these might include:

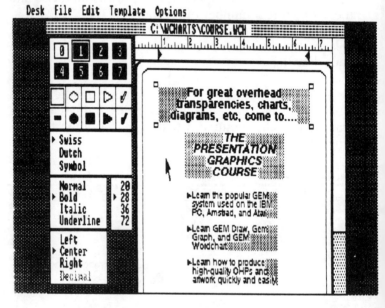

*Figure 7.3*   A GEM Wordchart display

- A zone in a large typeface, centred, for the title or main heading.
- A multiline zone in a smaller type for a list of topics.
- A further zone, perhaps in italics, to give a date and a venue.

The software provides you with a number of templates, consisting of predefined zones each of which occupies a certain size and generates a certain text font. The layout and sizes of the zones, and the choice of fonts, have been selected by design experts, so you are assured of a good-looking result, and you can customize the design – i.e. alter the zone sizes and the fonts – to meet the needs of a particular presentation.

It is a quick and simple job to type text into zones, and to make any adjustments that you require. Normally, to produce a wordchart ready for printing takes just a few minutes.

## 7.5 Graphing software

This allows you to produce good-looking charts and graphs (such as bar charts and line graphs) from data which you type in or import from a spreadsheet package. Most spreadsheet packages will incorporate graphing facilities; however, they will normally lack the capabilities of a dedicated graphics package, so the range of options they provide will be much more limited.

Having typed in or imported your data into the charting

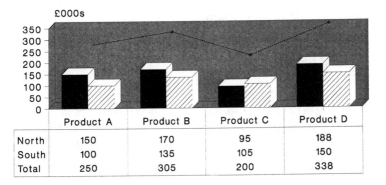

## Sales for XYZ Computer Co.
### 1990

£000s

|       | Product A | Product B | Product C | Product D |
|-------|-----------|-----------|-----------|-----------|
| North | 150       | 170       | 95        | 188       |
| South | 100       | 135       | 105       | 150       |
| Total | 250       | 305       | 200       | 338       |

Area

North  South  Total

*Figure 7.4* A chart produced in Harvard Graphics

package, you can select from a range of chart types (bar chart, pie chart, area chart, line graph, etc.) and a range of titling, labelling, and other options, and create, in a very automatic way, good-looking charts. The kind of thing that's possible is shown in Figure 7.4, produced in Harvard Graphics.

## 7.6  Presentation software

Presentation software such as Harvard Graphics or Lotus Freelance allow you to:

- Create many different types of drawings, charts, and graphs within the one package (rather than having to use separate packages as in the case of the GEM system).
- Present these pictures as a computer slide show, i.e. display them in sequence on a suitable monitor with various transition effects between successive charts.

Harvard Graphics incorporates 'hypershow' facilities, which allow you to create 'buttons' on slides which, when clicked on with the mouse, branch to other parts of the slide show. Also, you can create a 'run-time' version of your slide show, which can be run on other PCs without the need for Harvard Graphics itself to be present.

## 7.7  Desktop publishing

Most word processors can be used for simple desktop publishing (DTP). You can design a form or a simple magazine using a WP package, and print it out as a master for offset litho or photocopying. The problem is that you cannot normally produce either the wide variety of fonts that are possible with conventional typesetting, or the pictures or other graphics. And WP packages do not give you such a complete control over the final appearance of the printed page.

The advent of low-cost laser printers in 1985 brought typesetting within the reach of the ordinary microcomputer user. These devices can print any kind of text or graphics effects, a capability that was not lost on Apple Computers. Together with a company called Adobe, they brought out the Postscript page description language, which is a piece of software that enables laser printers to produce typesetting fonts and other effects. Another company called Aldus brought out PageMaker, a software package that enabled Apple Macintosh users to 'make up' pages on the screen, i.e. insert text and graphics material and organize its layout ready for printing. With this, the DTP revolution was born.

There are, today, a variety of page make-up packages, running not only on the Macintosh but on other computers as well. The PC is well supported, with a good version of PageMaker as well as Ventura Publisher and other page make-up software.

### 7.8 DTP and typesetting compared

The production of books, magazines, and other published material by conventional typesetting involves the following steps:

1 Authoring the original material, often using a WP package.
2 Editing the author's work, and annotating it with instructions to the typesetters on the fonts to be used and the layout of the material.
3 Typesetting the material, i.e. keying it into the typesetting equipment or transferring it electronically from the author's disks, laying it out on the screen, inserting control codes for various fonts, leaving spaces for pictures and diagrams, and printing the masters.
4 Pasting onto the master the pictures and diagrams.
5 Printing the final copies using an offset-litho printer.

With desktop publishing, steps 1 to 4 can all be done on the same system. The author's original material is imported into a page make-up package, where it can be laid out on the screen, merged electronically with any pictures and graphics, and have suitable fonts inserted. Once the page is right, it can be printed on a laser printer, ready for the offset-litho.

The advantages of using DTP rather than traditional typesetting are:

- The publication remains under your complete control.
- You can try out different designs and fonts, and see their effects immediately.
- You can produce the final result much more quickly.
- By eliminating the typesetter you can cut costs.

Furthermore, once word processors with full DTP facilities appear (or DTP packages with full word processing facilities appear), the authoring and the page make-up can be done on the same system, and, if required, at the same time. Microsoft's Word for Windows is an example of a WP package with good DTP facilities.


## 7.9   Hypermedia programs

Hypermedia programs are so-called because they span a variety of media, including pictures and music. They enable the user to store, retrieve, and manipulate information in all forms – data, text, image, and sound. Because of the large amount of computer storage space occupied by some of these forms of information – especially image – optical discs may be used in some hypermedia applications.

The term 'information base' could be used of material stored in a hypermedia application. Unlike the material in a database, which is stored in a highly structured form (remember the fields and records of Chapter 6), the material in a hypermedia application can take any form and will be stored in a quite unstructured way. What a hypermedia program does is to allow you to set up links between any item in the information base and any other item, and then to explore relationships by retrieving linked items.

You can visualize the items of information in an information base as places on a map, and the links between them as roads. As you extract one linked item after another, you are, in effect, taking one of many possible routes through the information. In a sizeable information base, there are a large number of links, resulting in a vast number of possible routes.

Here's one example. In an information base of pictures, a photograph of a building might be linked to a piece of text about a photographer, which might in turn be linked to other photos taken by the same person. It might also be linked to some text on architecture, and then to other photographs of buildings. As well as this, part of the building might be linked to a further close up photograph, or to other photographs of similar features.

To give another example, an information base might consist of a main piece of text – such as a report – and a number of subsidiary notes. Links might be set up between key words and phrases in the main document and material in the notes.

The existence of links attached to a word or phrase, or to a picture or part of a picture, can be indicated on the screen, so prompting you as to the possible routes that can be taken through the material from that point. In the case of the above example of a main document and subsidiary notes, words or phrases with links attached might be highlighted in some way. You select the word that you wish to explore further, usually by clicking on it with the mouse. The linked note then appears in a window on the screen. When you have finished with the note, you can click again to return to your place in the main document.

At the present time, the most well-known hypermedia program is Hypercard, which runs on the Apple Mac. As its name implies, this program stored information in the form of an electronic card index, each screenful of information occupying a card. An item of information on one card is linked to items on other cards by setting up 'buttons', i.e. symbols on the screen which you click with mouse to move from one item to another linked item.

## 7.10 Computer animation programs

Computer animation, using packages such as Autodesk's Animator, is becoming popular for creating presentations and demonstrations. By linking the computer with video equipment (see below), video images can be incorporated. The final output can be displayed on the computer's monitor in the normal way, or else converted to a video signal and recorded on video tape for playback on an ordinary video recorder.

In essence, an animation package such as Autodesk's Animator (Figure 7.5) is a painting program with animation features, with facilities which include the ability to take in and edit video pictures. You create a series of still images, called *frames*, link them in an animated sequence called a *flic*, and combine flics to produce a presentation.

Animator allows you to create five types of animation:

- *Cel animation*, i.e. Disney-style frame-by-frame animation of a series of individually-created frames.
- *Fly-by* optical effects, i.e. animating the movement of a piece of text or other image from one location and orientation on the screen to another by automatically generating the intermediate positions and orientations.
- *Polymorphic tweening*, i.e. turning one shape into another by automatically generating intermediate frames.
- *Titling animation* to scroll text in any direction.
- *Colour cycling* allowing you to automatically cycle through a range of colours over a sequence of frames.

To facilitate this, Animator provides 22 painting and animation 'tools', ranging from simple tools such as *Box* (to draw a box) and *Circle* (to draw a circle) to highly sophisticated tools such as *Tween* (to generate polymorphic tweening between a start position and shape and an end position and shape).

## 7.11 Multimedia applications

*Multimedia* refers to the convergence of audio, video, and other technologies with computer technology. As explained in Chapter 1, this convergence is facilitated by the trend towards the digitization of all forms of information, including digital audio systems, digital TV, and so on. By harnessing the computer to these various media technologies, powerful training, entertainment, and presentation systems can be created. They are described in the remaining sections of this chapter.

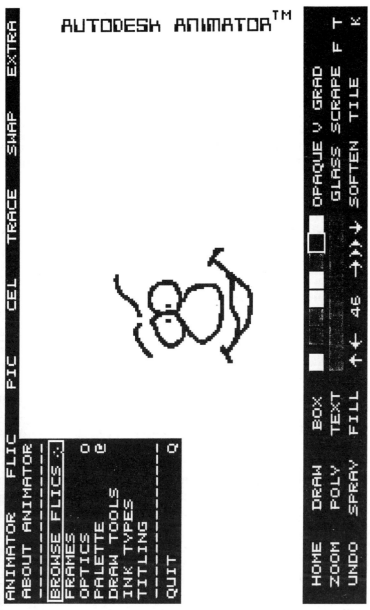

*Figure 7.5* An Autodesk Animator screen

Multimedia applications often involve the use of the computer to control equipment such as videodisc players, and mixing the video images with the computer's own output. It also includes the use of the PC with equipment such as video cameras and microphones to capture and edit video and audio input. At present, the main multimedia technologies and applications are:

• Interactive video, used mainly for training.
• Computer animation, using products such as Autodesk's Animator (see above), incorporating video and audio material.
• The use of data compression techniques to greatly reduce the amount of disk space occupied by video and other images. Compression ratios of over 100:1 are possible.

## 7.12   Interactive video

*Interactive video systems* (IV) allow the viewer to control a video programme using a computer. In practice, this means that the computer and video output appear together on the screen, the computer output often taking the form of either questions on the video sequence just seen, or else a menu of choices for further sequences. The viewer makes his or her response by typing at the keyboard, and the computer acts on this to determine which sequences of the video programme are played next.

IV can be achieved by linking a modified home video recorder to a computer. However, videodisc is a much better medium, for reasons which are explained in the next section.

The main application of IV is in education and training. The videodisc in this case will normally consist of many short sequences, each one lasting just a few minutes. The video is controlled by computer software in the form of a training package written using a special programming language called an authoring language. This software carries out the following tasks:

- It controls the order in which the video sequences are to be played. This can be modified by the learner, either by selecting menu choices or through the way in which he or she responds to questions. A learner with difficulties may be routed by the program through different sequences to a learner that answers the questions correctly.
- It displays questions on the screen to test the learner's understanding of the video sequence just seen.
- It matches the learner's response to a question against a number of possible responses that are stored in the program, and so marks it right or wrong.
- It provides feedback to the user, encouraging him in the case of correct answers and giving explanations in the case of incorrect answers.
- It keeps track of the learner's score for assessment purposes, and of the parts of the course that he or she found difficult.

IV has been found to be a very effective training tool. It has the following advantages over conventional training methods:

- Because the video sequences are interspersed with computer question-and-answer sequences, the learner has to apply his learning at frequent and regular intervals, which helps him retain and understand the material.
- The computer gives immediate feedback when the learner has typed an answer, and provides remedial instruction in the case of wrong answers. This is highly motivating, as well as ensuring that the learner has understood each point.
- The learner's route through the material can be geared to his or her needs.
- Because an impersonal machine rather than a human tutor is assessing his work, the learner is less embarrassed and demotivated by wrong answers.
- The material can be presented in a form which is visually attractive and stimulating.

Another major application of IV is point-of-sale (POS). Customers are able to quickly access video sequences on the products that interest them, or find out more about the services offered by a bank or other institution. IV has been successfully used in DHSS offices, where it allows clients to determine their rights and benefits without needing to speak with an official.

## 7.13   Videodisc

IV can be based upon videotape or videodisc. The former is relatively low-cost, and can incorporate video material produced fairly cheaply by the training institution itself. However, it has a number of disadvantages compared to the more sophisticated videodisc system described later:

- It takes a long time to wind through the tape to the start of a video sequence, unless that sequence is very close to the previous one.
- It cannot pinpoint sequences in the precise way that is possible with videodisc.
- It cannot pause on a video frame without distorting the image on the screen and, ultimately, wearing out the tape at that point.
- Programming the computer-based material for videotape is time-consuming, owing to the slow search time and the lack of an accurate frame numbering system.

For these reasons, videodisc material is much more suitable for IV.

The two main videodisc systems are Laservision (developed by Philips) and JVC's VHD system (which is based on electrical capacitance rather than on the optical technology described below). Both types of disc are 30 cm across, the same size as long-play music records.

Laservision discs store information in the form of tiny pits burned by laser light in the disc's surface. Unlike compact discs, laservision discs work on analogue rather than digital principles: the pits are in fact 'slices' of the waves recorded on them, as shown in Figure 7.6. Both the width of the pits and angles of the edges vary, and on playback these variations are measured by a narrow laser beam which is reflected from them onto the reading head of the laservision

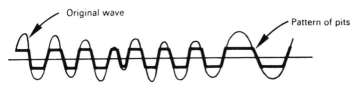

*Figure 7.6*    Pattern of pits on a Laservision disc

player. There is no physical contact between the surface of the disc and the reading head, so Laservision discs are not worn out by repeated playings.

Laservision discs for interactive video are called *active play* discs. Each circular track of an active play disc stores one complete video frame (picture). The player rotates the disc at a constant angular velocity of 25 revolutions per second to play back the video at the standard speed of 25 frames per second.

If you think about this, you will realize that, unlike an ordinary music record, the player must spin the disc faster when it is reading the outer tracks of the disc than when it is reading the inner tracks. This makes for a complex playback mechanism, but it provides the user with a very versatile system:

- If the reading head is held stationary over one rotating track, one frame is reproduced and held on the screen. The reproduction is perfect, unlike the awful picture you get when you try to hold a videotape on a single frame. This means that you can use a videodisc to store still pictures, such as sets of slides. An active-play disc can store 36 minutes of video per side, and since each second of video playback uses 25 frames, it is easy to work out the number of still pictures that can be stored on one side of a disc:

   $36 \times 60 \times 25 = 54,000$ pictures.

- Each frame can be identified by a number, and the player can access any frame simply by moving the reading head to the corresponding track. Any frame from the 54,000 stored on a side of a disc can be accessed in under 2 seconds. It is this numbering system that is used by the associated computer software to control the videoplayer.

To make a videodisc, the video sequences must first be shot using the professional C-format video system. When the final tape is edited and ready, a videodisc master is produced from it using a laser light process, and the individual discs are pressed from this.

The production of the video film is the most expensive part of the process, though other elements, such as writing the associated computer program, are not cheap. The total cost of producing an interactive videodisc, with the software, is likely to exceed £100,000. As a result, IV training packages are expensive, often several hundred pounds per copy – which is why there are not too many of them around in colleges. Nevertheless, IV packages are widely used in a number of big companies, where the large numbers who use them make this powerful training medium a cost-effective tool.

## 7.14   Compact discs

Compact discs are now widely used for music recordings. As explained in Chapter 3, compact discs store information in a digital form, which means that, unlike ordinary analogue recordings, there is no degradation of the signal. If the reproduction is less than perfect, then the fault lies with the other analogue parts of the system – such as the microphones and the loudspeakers – rather than the compact discs themselves.

Being digital, compact discs clearly have an important role in the digital world of IT. For besides audio recordings, they can be used to store computer data and text, as well as video images in digital form. Interactive video systems based upon compact disc are likely to be much more significant in the future than IV systems based on videodisc.

Laser light represents a binary 1 by a short pulse of light from a laser gun, and a binary 0 by the absence of a pulse. To record information on a compact disc, very powerful pulses of laser light are used, which burn tiny pits in its surface. As the disc rotates, and the laser gun works its way like a gramophone stylus across the surface, a tightly-packed spiral of tracks consisting of thousands of tiny pits is built up.

On playback, the process works in reverse. A low-powered laser beam scans the tracks of the rotating disc, being reflected back by the silvered surface. The pits on the surface are 1/4 of the wavelength of the laser light in depth, so light reflected from the bottom of a pit is exactly out of phase with light reflected from the surface. It therefore interferes with it, largely cancelling it out. The returning beam strikes a photoelectric cell, which converts the light to electric pulses. The less intense light from a pit produces a smaller pulse than light reflected from a spot on the surface which doesn't contain a pit. In this way the original pattern of 1s and 0s is reproduced.

As with videodisc, there is no physical contact between the surface of the disc and the playback mechanism, and so no wear is caused by repeated playings, and grease or dust normally has no affect. Unlike videodisc, a compact disc is only 5.25″ across, the same as an ordinary floppy disk.

## 7.15   Compact disc for multimedia applications

The huge capacity of compact discs means that they can store large amounts of computer data, text, images, and sound. Encyclopaedias, for example, are now being published in compact disc form. This not only makes them very compact, it also means that, since they can be linked to the power of the computer, all entries on a selected topic can be rapidly retrieved and displayed on the screen.

Another development is *CD-V*, short for 'Compact Disc – Video', which will be used for high-quality sound and video. One obvious application for CD-V is pop videos.

There are also interesting possibilities of computer-controlled multimedia presentations using compact disc systems. These could form a low-cost alternative to IV systems. Philips, for example, has been working for a number of years on *CD-I*, which stands for 'Compact Disc – Interactive', and is bringing out a mass-market CD-I player in 1992. (A professional system is already available.) This will cost a fraction of the price of a videodisc player, and will use comparatively inexpensive compact discs. Quite a number of CD-I discs are currently being produced ready for the launch, covering topics as diverse as photography, golf, and language learning.

CD-I aims to take full advantage of the enormous capacity of compact discs for storing images and sounds as well as text, and combine this with the power of the computer to develop a new publishing medium. This will revolutionize encyclopaedias, dictionaries, training materials, and so on, which ideally contain visual, aural, and textual components. A single disc is able to hold a complete English-language dictionary, including the words in audio and some accompanying pictures in (still) video.

Like interactive video, the computer software will allow the user to access any part of the disc by means of a system of menus or questions, and if necessary will conduct him through the disc as part of a training package, with questions, feedback, and branching.

Unlike interactive video, the pictures are digitized, and have to be read from the disc and processed by the computer before they can be displayed on the screen. The Philips machine will have two video processors, which means that it can display simultaneously two different signals from the disc, e.g. text and real pictures. So it can be used in much the same way as interactive video, at a fraction of the (hardware) price.

Two competing multimedia compact disc systems that have already reached the market are Intel's Digital Video Interactive (DVI) system and Commodore's CDTV (Commodore Dynamic Total Vision). At the moment, Philips CD-I seems to be technically superior, but things change rapidly in the highly competitive world of computing and multimedia.

## 7.16   Data compression

In order to reduce the amount of space occupied by video images, data compression techniques are employed. Intel's DVI chip set, for example, can achieve compression ratios of around 160:1. The speed of compression (to store the image) and decompression (to reproduce the image) are very fast, and we are not far off the day when full-motion high-resolution video can be reproduced by a PC from compressed files.

Data compression uses the fact that a great deal of information in an image or sequence of images is redundant. For example, expanses of sky do not change from pixel to pixel within an individual frame, nor from frame to frame within a sequence of frames. This redundant data can therefore be thrown out, all that is needed is the data for a single pixel together with the area of the frame, and the sequence of frames, to which it applies.

A variety of mathematical techniques are used to increase the amount of compression. For example, the Philips CD-I system employs a compression technique called *Discrete Cosine Transform* (DCT), which breaks down each frame into blocks, and compares how these change from frame to frame. If there is little change from frame to frame the blocks can be bigger, and less code is therefore needed to produce a succession of frames.

### 7.17   Virtual reality systems

You have probably seen examples of interactive video material, such as the BBC's Domesday Project, perhaps on TV. If so, you will know that many videodiscs include numerous shots of buildings, streets, or towns taken from many angles, and that the computer-driven interactive part of the system allows you to 'travel' around the building or town. Unlike an ordinary film, with this system you can choose which way to go (by perhaps pointing and clicking with the mouse), and you can pause in any location and look around before proceeding.

It's a bit like real life, except that it only impacts your visual senses – you can't, for example, touch any of the objects you are looking at, and you are always aware that you are not really 'there' but are in fact sat in front of a monitor. But what if you could 'touch' the objects, and what if you could see them in three dimensions on a wrap-around screen. And what if you could move around by some more natural means than pushing and clicking a mouse?

Well, systems are around that can do this, and they

transport the user into a 'virtual reality' – something that closely simulates real life.

Virtual reality systems were first developed by NASA in the mid 1980s, to solve the problem of repairing space stations. Ideally, it wanted to use robots to work in the hostile environment of space, but there are repair situations where the human skills are essential. Its solution was to feed signals from the video camera in the robot's 'head' to the human astronaut on the ground, and relay back to the robot the movements of the astronaut's hands. So a headset was developed containing two tiny TV sets, one for each eye, to give stereo vision. It also contained tracking circuitry to transmit movements of the astronaut's head to the robot, so that the camera automatically pointed wherever the astronaut wished to look. The astronaut also wore a *dataglove* which could transmit the movements of his hands and fingers to the robot.

Today, half a decade later, virtual reality systems have progressed considerably:

- The headset now contains stereo earphones for sound.
- The user may sit in a console of some kind which simulates the movement of aircraft or other transportation.
- In many virtual reality applications, the whole system is hooked up to a computer, which generates the simulated environment. In these systems the dataglove will be programmed to interpret certain movements as commands. For example, if you wish to move through the simulated environment, you simply point your finger in the desired direction.
- Instead of a dataglove it is now possible to don an entire 'datasuit' so that movements of the entire body can be electronically sensed and transmitted.

Virtual reality applications include:

- Flight test simulators.
- Control of robots and other devices in environments that are impossible for humans. Space station maintenance has already been mentioned, but future possibilities seem limitless, from microsurgery (by controlling a tiny

surgical device inserted in the patient's body) to testing the design of buildings by walking through computer simulations of them.

- Entertainment and leisure applications, such as computer 'arcade' games.

# 8
# Computer communications

## 8.1 What is computer communications?

Computer communications is to do with the transfer of information by:

- Direct connection by cable of two computers.
- Connection of two computers via the public telephone system or other telecommuications links.
- Networking of a number of computers.

In the first part of this chapter I shall deal with the equipment, software, and procedures involved in computer communications, and in the second part I shall cover some of the telecommunications services that are available, such as telex, fax and videoconferencing.

There are a number of reasons why you might want to connect your computer with others:

- To transfer files between your computer and a different type of computer with incompatible disks. For example, you might wish to transfer a document written on a PC to an Apple Mac running a DTP system.
- To send messages to people with other computers, and to receive messages from them. This is called electronic mail, or *email* for short.
- To access information stored on other remote computers, such as sales, inventory, and other internal information in the case of your organization's computers, or financial and economic information in the case of public systems.

● To update your organization's computer files when you are away from base.
● To share files with other users in your office or organization.

In the case of computers within the same office, there are additional reasons why you might want them permanently connected together in a local area network. These were dealt with in Chapter 3, and include the fact that you can share resources (such as hard disks and printers), software, and files, and the fact that a centralized backup facility operated by the network manager increases the security of data.

## 8.2   Communications concepts

The four basic communications concepts that you need to know are *RS-232*, *baud rate*, *protocol*, and *bandwidth*.

1   *RS-232*.   This is the main communications standard in the computer world, defining the connections to be used in the cabling that links computers. It specifies a channel for transmitting data, a channel for receiving data, and channels for control signals. It also specifies that data is transmitted serially, i.e. one bit at a time, and so the RS-232 socket on a computer is often called the *serial* port.

2   *Baud rate*.   This refers to the number of bits of data per second (bps) that are transmitted over a communications link. The RS-232 standard does not specify a single baud rate, but it allows a number of rates: 75, 150, 300, 600, up to 9600 and above. Commonly-used rates are 300 and 1200. Many on-line systems (such as bulletin boards) send and receive data at either 300 or 1200 baud. One exception, though, is Prestel – when connected to this, you send data from your computer at 75 baud, and receive it from the Prestel computer at 1200 baud. Before you can use your computer to communicate, you must set its baud rate. You will normally do this using communications software (see below).

3   *Protocol*.   Besides the baud rate, there are other 'hand-shaking' protocols that have to be set before communi-

cations can take place between computers. These include parity, stop bits, and other things which, fortunately, you can normally leave to your communications software to look after.

4   *Bandwidth*.   This measures the amount of information that can be transmitted through a medium (such as a telephone wire) in a second. Conventional communications systems, such as much of the telephone network, transmit information in the form of waves, in which case the bandwidth is measured by the range of frequencies, in KHz, that the medium allows. (KHz means 1000 hertz, and 1 hertz = 1 cycle per second.)

To an increasing extent, though, communications systems transmit information in digital form, i.e. in pulses, and in these cases bandwidth is measured by the number of bits per second (bps) that can travel through the medium.

## 8.3   Hardware and software

What do you need for computer communications?

- To get your computer communicating with another, you need communications software and a suitable cable.
- If you wish to carry out these communications via the telephone network, you need a modem.
- To network your computer to others in your office, you need a local area network.

Let's look at each of these.

## 8.4   Communications software

A large number of communications packages are available, especially for the PC, and some of these are in the public domain (and therefore free).

Notable public domain packages are Kermit and Procomm. Kermit is primarily for transferring files between different types of computer, and it is available for more than 200 computers, ranging from home micros to mainframes. It is available in this country from the Kermit Distribution Service, Lancaster University. Procomm is a popular PC package for communicating with bulletin boards or other computers via the telephone, and this is available from PC user groups or public domain software distributors such as Compulink, The Sanctuary, Oakhill Grove, Surbiton, Surrey.

Some popular commercial comms programs for the PC are Crosstalk, Smarterm, and Chit-Chat. Chit-Chat is a UK product marketed by Sage. It costs almost £100, but it offers some features which are not available in public domain software. For example, it enables the PC to handle viewdata systems such as Prestel, and it comes with a library of telephone numbers of UK bulletin boards and on-line databases.

## 8.5   Modems

The word *modem* is short for modulator/demodulator, terms used to describe a device which enables you to send and receive signals via a telephone carrier wave. If you want to communicate with other computers via the telephone line, you have to convert your computer's digital output to an analogue (i.e. wave-like) telephone signal, and convert the incoming analogue signal to digital computer input. Hence the need for a modem, linking your computer to the telephone socket.

As with other computer hardware, there are many models on the market, and a number of standards. However, the most common standard is that set by the Hayes modem, so it's a good idea to purchase either a Hayes or Hayes-compatible modem. Prices vary, depending on the features. The cheapest and least satisfactory, are acoustic modems. These cost only about £50, but they require you to dial up manually and place the telephone receiver in an acoustic box. Not only is this awkward, it also means that any extraneous noises can interfere with the signal, corrupting the data being sent or received.

Nowadays, few modems use an acoustic link. Instead, electronics within the modem converts between computer and telephone signals. On cheaper models you may still have to dial manually, the procedure being to switch over to the computer and replace the receiver when the connection is made. Most modems, though, are fully automatic, allowing dial-up via the computer, either by keying in the number at the keyboard or by selecting from a library of numbers stored on disk.

As well as these differences, cheap modems offer a very restricted choice of communications speeds, perhaps only the most common speed of 300 baud. Mid-range modems generally offer not only 300 baud but 1200 baud as well (also widely used, and four times as fast), and the split speeds used by viewdata systems of 1200/75 (i.e. 1200 baud to receive data, 75 baud to transmit). More expensive modems offer higher speeds as well, allowing for very fast (and therefore inexpensive) data communications.

To use a modem, you have to connect it to the computer using an RS-232 cable, unless it is an internal modem that sits inside the computer's casing. You also have to connect it to the telephone socket. The modem's telephone cable may be supplied with a two-way adaptor which fits into the wall socket, in which case both it and your phone can be plugged in at the same time.

With most modems, your communications software will enable you to set the baud rate and other handshaking protocols, and to dial up the number of the remote computer.

## 8.6  Local area networks

Local area networks, or LANs, are used to link up a number of computers and other peripheral devices on the same site. They enable users to share applications software, datafiles, peripherals such as printers, and common services provided by the network manager such as daily file backup.

A LAN consists of a single cable laid around the site, with sockets along its length for connecting the computers, printers, and other devices. Data from the devices is sent round the network in small chunks or *packets*, each of which includes the 'address' of the destination machine.

As explained in Chapter 3, one of the computers in a network is the *file-server*, meaning that it handles the network filing system and directly controls the hard disk containing the application software and files. The other computers are called *terminals*, *stations*, or *clients*. Any network operating system command issued at a station (e.g. to retrieve a file from the hard disk) is passed along the cable to the file-server, which acts on the command and transmits the output – for instance data read from a file – along the cable to the terminal.

A major problem with networks is ensuring that messages from one station do not interfere with those from another, resulting in both messages getting scrambled and lost. There are a number of possible solutions to this problem, resulting in different types of network system. The two most popular are Ethernet and IBM's Token Ring network.

- In the Ethernet system, a station wishing to send information checks if there are any messages (packets) travelling round the cable. If there are not, it sends its message. If two stations, by chance, do this simultaneously, their messages interfere with each other and are lost. However, the fact that this has happened is signalled back to the two stations, and they each then wait a short random length of time and try again.

- In the Token Ring system, an electronic signal called a *token* circulates around the network, passing from station to station. A station cannot send a message until it has the token, so avoiding the possibility of two stations transmitting simultaneously.

As with most things in the computer world, messaging takes place very rapidly, whichever network system is used. Ethernet has the advantage that it is relatively inexpensive to install, since it requires a simpler cabling system. It has also become the major networking standard, being accepted by a large number of manufacturers. It is probably the best system for small networks.

The Token Ring system, in contrast, requires more elaborate cabling and a central PC dedicated to controlling the network. It is, however, a more robust system (i.e. it is less likely to fail) than Ethernet, and it is faster. It is probably the most suitable system for large networks with long lengths of cabling.

A variety of network operating systems are available for PCs, most of which will run on both the Ethernet and Token Ring systems. The most popular is Netware (from Novell), which will work on most types of network. To the user, there is little difference running software over a network to running it from floppy disk under DOS, except that some things happen rather more slowly.

Most application packages will work over a network, though problems can arise if more than one user is trying to write to the same data or text file. Many packages have special versions for networks that provide file or record 'locking' to ensure that only one person at a time can write to a file or record.

Local area networks can be linked via telecommunications networks (see below), to become a *wide area network* (WAN).

## 8.7 Telecommunications

'Telecommunications' means 'communications at a distance'. Telecommunications technology embraces radio waves travelling through the air or through space, electrical waves flowing along a telephone wire, and laser pulses travelling along optical fibres (see below).

In the case of wave-based telecommunications, a single-frequency carrier wave is modulated with the waveform of the speech or other transmitted message. Many carrier waves, each of a different frequency, can travel along a wire or through the air, and so many conversations can take place at the same time along the same wire or over radio waves. Your radio or TV receiver, for example, allows you to pick up any of these by tuning it to the appropriate carrier wave frequency.

To use this system for computer communications, the digital signal from the computer has to be converted to a wave form at the transmitting end, and back to digital form at the receiving end hence the need for modems, as explained earlier.

With the steady computerization of all aspects of our lives, more and more computer data is travelling along telephone wire. In addition, the telephone network itself is becoming computer controlled. It makes sense, therefore, to convert the network to handle data in the same way as computers do, i.e. as digital pulses rather than as waves.

This is now being done, spurred on by developments in telecommunications technology which enables far more data to be transmitted along digital circuits than is possible over the analogue (wave form) circuits. Because these new circuits have such a wide bandwidth, they are sometimes called *broadband* circuits.

Optical fibre cables are one example. To cope with ever-increasing computer communications, British Telecom is laying these across the country to link its main switching centres. Data will travel along these thin glass fibres in the form of pulses of laser light. The bandwidth of this medium is so high that a single fibre can carry almost half of the voice telephone traffic of the country.

(If the whole telephone network were converted to digital communications, ordinary telephone conversations would have to be digitized to use the system, and then be converted back to sound waves at the receiving end. The device that does this is called a *codec* – short for 'coder-decoder' – and in a digital system one of these is needed in every telephone handset.)

The advantages of digital over analogue communications are as follows:

- All information, whether voice, image, text, or data, is sent in a common digital form that can be handled by computer-based equipment. Every kind of transmission, whether phone, video, or computer data, can therefore share the same network. Modems, essential for sending data over the analogue network, are unnecessary. ISDN, short for 'integrated services digital network', is the name given to this system.
- Since the information sent over the network can be handled by computer, a number of new facilities are possible. British Telecom's digital service offers over 50 new facilities that were not previously available.

Information in digital form is less prone to line noise and degradation than information in analogue form. This is because the equipment can easily distinguish a pulse from the absence of a pulse, and so separate it

from the accompanying noise. So voice calls, for example, will be much clearer.
● Digital communications offer the possibility of broadband communications (e.g. using optical fibre technology) so enabling more information to be sent at lower cost.

Around 160 countries intend to support the ISDN standard. British Telecom's ISDN service has been around for some time and its use is growing. It offers a data transmission rate of 64,000 bits per second, much faster than the highest rates that can be achieved using a modem over the analogue network. However, BT's ISDN service is expensive at present, and only large corporations can justify its use. One day, no doubt, it will be much cheaper and will completely replace the ubiquitous analogue telephone network.

(Note that computers are not able to connect directly to the ISDN network, as computer data, though digital, is not in the form required for transmission over the network. What's called *network terminating equipment* (NTE) is needed. In the case of PCs, NTE cards are available that can be slotted inside the computer's casing.)

## 8.8   Circuit switching and packet switching

At present, most telephone networks are *circuit switched*. This means that each device is connected to a switching centre (telephone exchange), which handles all message routing. When a circuit linking transmitter to receiver is set up, it is dedicated to the call, and cannot be used for any other purpose until the call is finished. This has two disadvantages:

● It wastes telecommunications resources, because for a significant part of most calls no information is being exchanged, and the circuit is therefore unused.
● One device cannot communicate with another if all the lines are engaged or if the latter is itself making a call.

To overcome these problems, *packet switching* is being introduced. As in local area networks, the data is transmit ted in addressed 'packets', each one up to 512 bits long. The computers controlling the switching centres read the addresses and route the packets accordingly.

Unlike circuit switching, the lines are not dedicated to individual calls, and some packets making up a call may travel by a different route to other packets. However, each packet contains information giving its position in the sequence of packets that make up the message, and so it can be properly sequenced upon arrival at its destination. If necessary, the network is able to store the complete message until the addressee is available to receive it.

This means that telephone lines can be utilized with much greater efficiency than before, and problems of engaged lines do not occur. Another change that is planned when the system is fully implemented is that the cost of using the network is dependent solely on the amount of information transmitted, not upon the distance it is sent. In this sense it will be similar to the postal services – it costs as much to send a package to the other end of the country as it does to send it to the next town.

Another advantage of digital networks is the fact that the rate at which data is transmitted can be varied in different parts of the network, so that:

- The network can respond flexibly to changes in the volume of traffic and the type of communication link.
- Devices with differing baud rates can intercommunicate via the network.

## 8.9   The Open Systems Interconnection (OSI) reference model

The OSI model defines a set of networking and telecommunications standards. By complying with these standards, different hardware and software manufacturers ensure that their products are compatible. (It is no good attempting to link up different makes of equipment on a network if they are not compatible, as they will not be able to communicate.)

The OSI standards are widely accepted. They divide

networking issues into *layers* numbered 1 (the most basic) to 7 (the most complex):

- Layer 1 is the most basic, covering the physical connections. Twisted-wire pairs, coaxial, and optical fibre cabling are all defined by this layer.
- Layer 2 defines protocols, i.e. how the data that travels around the network is to be encoded and decoded.
- Layer 3 defines how data should be routed through the network. Single channel networks, such as most LANs, do not need this level.
- Layer 4 deals with error handling across the network, and flow control.
- Layer 5 defines how communications sessions between network devices are to be managed.
- Layer 6 defines how menus, colours, characters, and so on are to be encoded as control sequences for transmission across the network. SQL, for example, sits within this layer and conforms to it.
- Layer 7 defines how application packages are to use the network.

## 8.10    Telecommunications services

The remainder of this chapter covers the main telecommunications services that are of use to the office. They include the telephone and cellular radio, telex and fax, videophone, and video conferencing, as well as on-line databases and email.

## 8.11    Telephone

Although the telephone is one of the oldest of these services it has recently undergone a transformation in terms of developments and related services that have enhanced its usefulness. These include:

- Low-cost answering machines for receiving and recording incoming calls.
- Handsets offering features such as a memory for storing

and dialling frequently-used numbers and an automatic redial facility for engaged numbers.

- Computer-based facilities offered by Telecom's digital exchanges, such as automatic ring-back and tracing of malicious calls.
- Telephone conferencing so that several parties can be linked together in a single call.
- Cellular radio so that phones can be used in moving vehicles (see below).

Some new services being developed for subscribers in America but not yet available in this country are:

- Transmission of the caller's telephone number, so that it appears on a screen attached to the recipient's phone. This enables the latter to choose to answer, reject, or forward the call to another number.
- Call block, allowing recipients to program their phones to automatically reject calls from up to 12 known numbers.
- Priority screening, which gives priority treatment to calls from up to 12 selected numbers – the phone rings in a distinctive way when a priority number calls, and if the recipient is out, the number is stored in the telephone company's computer for later access by the recipient.
- Call forwarding, which automatically switches all calls or pre-selected calls to another number.
- Call answering, which works rather like an answering machine. Subscribers can leave a pre-recorded message on the telephone company's computer, which is automatically relayed to callers. They in turn can leave messages for the subscriber.

## 8.12   Cellular radio

Cellular radio is a computer-controlled mobile communications service made possible by the change-over to digital communications. Under this system, cellular radio sets, or 'mobiles', normally installed in cars, can communicate with each other and with ordinary phone users in the following way.

The country is split up into a large number of 'cells', each one being between two and twenty miles across (depending on whether the area covered is urban or rural) and having at its centre a base with a low-powered radio transmitter. This is able to transmit to and receive from any mobiles within the perimeter of the cell, and it is connected via a computer-controlled switching centre to the telephone network. Outside the perimeter the strength of the signal falls away, so that although bases in adjacent cells use different frequencies, one in a non-adjacent cell can use the same frequencies without risk of interference.

When a cellular radio subscriber keys in a telephone number, it is transmitted over a special control channel to the cell base, which passes it to the switching centre. The centre dials the number on the telephone network, and at the same time allocates a radio frequency to the mobile, which automatically switches to that frequency and so enables the user to make the call. If the subscriber drives from one cell to another while the call is in progress, the switching centre automatically switches transmitters and frequencies.

In the case of calls made to a mobile, the switching centre sends a paging signal on the control channel. The system will switch the paging transmission from cell to cell until it locates the set, the search being done in an intelligent manner by contacting first the set's home base and looking up the computer records of its last known location. The search time is never more than a few seconds.

## 8.13   Telex

Telex is a popular way of transmitting text over the telephone network, though for reasons which are explained below its use is declining, being replaced by facsimile.

Telex is transmitted and received by *teletypewriters*, which are a kind of communicating typewriter with a paper tape punch and a paper tape reader. Contact between two teletypes is established by dialling in the usual way, and the text may then be typed in to the transmitting teletype by the telex operator. However, in order to save on telephone line time, the message will normally be typed in and recorded on paper tape before the call takes place, and then read rapidly from the tape after dial-up.

Many major organizations are telex users, and until recently the service boasted over a million subscribers world-wide. Two factors contributed to this success:

- All telex machines observe common communications protocols, i.e. they are all compatible.
- There is a comprehensive directory of telex users.

However, facsimile and other text communication services are superseding telex (see below). The reason is that the transmission rate of telex is low (50 bps, i.e. about a word per second), which means that the length of each call, and therefore the phone charge, is relatively high.

## 8.14 Teletex

Teletex is an enhanced telex system designed to take advantage of modern digital packet-switched telecommunications systems. The transmission rate is 2400 bps, almost 50 times faster than telex. Although this system is expected eventually to take over from telex, its current usage is low because teletex standards have not been precisely specified, so there is some incompatibility between different manufacturers' machines.

## 8.15 Facsimile

Facsimile, or *fax* for short, was developed at the beginning of this century to transmit images, such as newspaper photographs, by telephone line. A fax machine contains a photoelectric cell which scans the image and converts the blacks, greys, and whites into electrical signals, which modulate the telephone carrier wave. The same device will also act as a receiver, able to decode incoming signals and print them as image on special paper. Nowadays, the 'images' that are transmitted by fax are usually pages of text.

Fax machines are grouped according to quality of scanning and reproduction. Group 1 machines give high quality results, with good differentiation between the various shades of grey. The amount of information that has to be transmitted in this case is high, and so the transmission time for an A4 document is a lengthy six minutes. Group 2 machines give lower quality results but cut the transmission time in half.

Of most interest so far as text transmission is concerned are the Group 3 and 4 machines, which give black and white results without grey tones. Unlike Group 1 and 2, these are digital machines, converting a black (or dark grey) dot on paper to a binary 1, and a white (or light grey) dot to a binary 0. They are well suited to digital communications, and the transmission time – and therefore the cost of each call – is very low. Current models are about the size of a small dot of matrix printer, and they can transmit an A4 page in just a few seconds.

In the past, the use of fax was inhibited by:

- The lack of a directory of users.
- The fact that fax machines differed widely in their transmission rates, so that one manufacturer's models could not communicate with those of another.

Today, however, there is a directory of users, and the digital Group 3 and 4 machines have standardized transmission rates. This, and the high transmission speeds, have brought about the boom in fax usage.

## 8.16    Videophones and videoconferencing

Nowadays, it is possible to see as well as hear a telephone caller by using a *videophone*, a device consisting of both a video system and a phone. The video system consists of a black-and-white video camera and a monitor.

An ordinary black-and-white video picture occupies the same bandwidth as 600 telephone conversations. To avoid prohibitively expensive calls, videophone systems transmit pictures intermittently, to give a series of still images rather than a continuously moving one. Also, they remove redundant information from the picture and use compression techniques to reduce the information that has to be sent.

The system can be used, for example, to send pictures of components for fault diagnosis, pictures of damaged parts of a patient's body in the health care field, or pictures of products in the field of retailing.

Video conferencing systems are also available, which allow several callers to hold meetings without needing to travel long distances. British Telecom's Confravision system provides this sort of service, linking major cities by a network of videoconferencing studios for remote meetings.

### 8.17   On-line databases and bulletin boards

There are a large number of on-line systems that can be accessed over the telephone line using a personal computer. The biggest are in the US, but there are a number of important ones in this country also.

An on-line system may provide *database*, *bulletin board*, and *email* facilities, sometimes just one or two of these, often all three. It may also provide a 'gateway' – i.e. a communications link – to other on-line databases, which you can access from it.

An on-line database mainly stores libraries of economic, financial, and statistical data, together with up-to-the-minute news from sources such as Reuters. It will normally be run on a large computer system, and subscribers will have to pay quarterly fees as well as being charged for the information accessed.

A bulletin board is more like a notice board, containing electronic messages, adverts, and informal 'chatting' and interchange of information by users. It is often a small affair, sometimes run by a single enthusiast using a low-cost computer system. A number of bulletin boards are free, so all you have to pay is the cost of the phone bill.

Systems that charge a fee normally provide a number of services, including email. Each subscriber is provided with an electronic 'mailbox', an area on the host computer's disk where messages to him from other users can be stored. He can also send messages to other users, addressing their mailbox by means of their username or number. Like ordinary mail, this kind of system is less immediate than ordinary voice calls but offers a number of advantages:

- There is no interruption factor – you can read all your email and answer them at a time convenient to yourself.
- The normal problems of telephone calls – engaged lines and recipient unavailability – are avoided.
- It may be cheaper than a phone call, especially if the recipient lives a long way away.
- A message can be sent to a number of subscribers at the same time.

Two major UK examples of on-line systems are British Telecom's *Prestel* and *Telecom Gold*. Other smaller systems include:

- Easylink, with links between the UK and the US, and ancillary services such as translation of email and telexes into French, German, and Spanish.
- Quik-Comm, an international email service.
- One To One, with email, translation, noticeboard, radio-paging, as well as access to other databases.

Recently, Compuserve, the enormous US on-line system, has expanded into Europe. This is described below.

## 8.18   Compuserve

In Europe, Compuserve has merged with Datamail, a large email service, and Datastar, a database service, to become Compuserve/FORUM. It is also linked with a number of other email networks, including the UK's JANET academic and research network. Compuserve is accessed via a number of communications networks, one in the UK being Istel.

Compuserve's own on-line service is called the Compuserve Information Service (CIS). This has about 600,000 subscribers, mainly in the US. It includes about 200 special-interest groups or *Forums*. Within a forum, you can leave bulletin-board messages, 'chat' (using a keyboard) with anyone else who happens to be logged on at the same time, and download software. There is a Microsoft Applications forum, for example, and a Lotus forum, as well as forums run by Apple, Atari, IBM, and many others. There are also a number of non-technical forums.

For researchers, CIS provides gateways to some 1,400 databases worldwide. For 800 of these, CIS provides its own front end that provides a common method of searching for information.

It also offers a flexible email service allowing you to send not only ASCII text files but also spreadsheet and graphics files, up to 512K long.

## 8.19   Electronic data interchange

Increasingly, computers of different organizations are being linked directly over the telephone line, so that ordering and invoicing can be done entirely electronically rather than by sending paper documents through the post. The technology that enables this is called *electronic data interchange* (EDI). The significance of this for business and manufacturing is described in Chapter 10.

EDI requires the provision of what's called *value-added data network services* (VADS). These are services which are added to the basic telecommunications network, and include:

- Speed conversion, enabling terminals with differing baud rates to communicate.
- Protocol conversion, enabling a terminal to communicate with other incompatible terminals.
- Connection and message-routing facilities.
- Store-and-forward, allowing messages to be stored for forwarding later.
- Gateways to other databases and services.

At the time of writing, there are some 5,000 EDI users in Europe out of a total potential market of around six million companies, but it is anticipated that EDI usage will grow rapidly during the 1990s.

# 9
# Data processing

## 9.1 What is data processing?

*Data processing*, as distinct from text (word) processing, image processing, or speech or music processing, refers to the use of the computer to record, store, retrieve, analyse, and communicate data. That data will often be in numerical form, but will include textual data such as names, addresses, product codes, and so on.

Data processing (DP) may include scientific and engineering 'number crunching' applications, but it mainly refers to the processing of business transactions, such as sales and purchases. The term *transaction processing* is sometimes used to distinguish the latter from scientific number crunching, and it is with transaction processing that we are primarily concerned in this chapter.

In small businesses, data (transaction) processing will normally be carried out on PCs, using off-the-shelf applications packages such as database packages and accounts packages. I dealt with this type of package in Chapter 6. In larger businesses, mainframe or minicomputers will be used, and software may be specially written by staff in a data processing department. This chapter is mainly concerned with DP procedures and organization in larger businesses.

## 9.2 Plan of this chapter

This chapter begins by introducing DP operations and procedures, and the advantages and disadvantages of using a computer for these. Then it examines DP issues regarding the collection of data, the input of data, and the storage and processing of data. Finally, it examines the role of the DP department, and the work of systems analysts in desinging data processing systems.

## 9.3 Data processing operations

The basic DP operations are those outlined in Chapter 1: recording data, storing and retrieving data, calculating/ analysing data, and communicating the results. For example, the operations needed to produce the week's payroll for a factory are:

1 Record the hours worked by each operative, perhaps using clock cards or time sheets.
2 Store this data temporarily, then retrieve it together with data held on the operatives' records (i.e. the wage rates, tax codes, and other deductions).
3 Calculate the wages due to each employee by multiplying the hours worked by the wage rate and subtracting the deductions.
4 Output the results of this processing onto the payroll, and also onto the wages slips, paycheques, or other payment documents, as well as to any reports that summarize, for example, labour costs.

A set of DP operations such as this is called a *procedure*. The clock cards or other documents that contain the input data are called *source documents*. The purpose of data processing is to produce the *transaction documents* needed by a business (such as invoices and purchase orders) and to produce the *reports* (analyses) needed to support decision-making by management. (For more information on transaction documents and reports, see page 16.)

We could use the flowchart symbols shown on page 90 to describe data processing procedures. A flowchart for an invoicing procedure is shown in Figure 9.1.

## 9.4 Advantages of computer data processing

The advantages of using computers for data processing are the same as their advantages for the other kinds of applica-

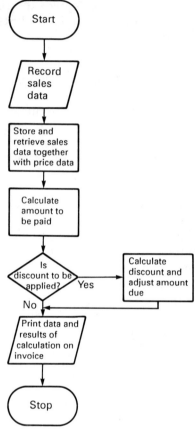

*Figure 9.1*   Invoicing flowchart

tion described in this book: they are fast, labour-saving, accurate, and cheap. Compared to data processing by manual methods, computer data processing offers the following specific advantages:

- The input, storage, calculating, and output devices are all linked electronically, so that once data on the source documents has been keyed in, all subsequent processing is quite automatic.
- Many of the documents that are used in manual systems to pass data from one procedure to another can be eliminated, for in a computer system the output from

one procedure can be stored electronically and then retrieved for use by another procedure. (Documents such as invoices, which travel between one firm and another, are still necessary, though electronic invoicing is starting to be used, and the day is not far off when direct communication between computers in different organizations will be commonplace.)

- Computers work at very high speeds, and so process data and produce output very rapidly. This is especially important in the case of reports for managers, who need up-to-date information on which to base their decisions.
- The fact that computer data processing is automatic can result in substantial savings in labour. It also means that human errors will not arise during processing.
- Computers contain few moving parts, so they are relatively inexpensive to manufacture and run, and very reliable.

## 9.5 Disadvantages of computer data processing

Computer data processing obviously has many advantages over manual processing. Many offices, in particular small offices, still retain manual methods, sometimes with good reason. For computers are not without their disadvantages:

- They have to be paid for. A small business system, with a decent printer, software, etc., will probably cost around two or three thousand pounds.
- Existing procedures have to be converted to computer processing. The change-over can be protracted, and can cause many headaches.
- A breakdown in the equipment can bring the entire office to a halt.
- Computer processing is more inflexible than manual processing. Once set up, the computer procedures cannot be as easily changed to cope with the changing requirements of a business.
- Computer security can be a major problem. Businesses have been defrauded of large sums of money by employees tampering with their computer systems.

Apart from computer security, these disadvantages are declining in importance with the steady reduction in costs and improvement in reliability and features of computer systems.

## 9.6   Coding systems

We are all familiar with coding systems. Examples include postcodes, employee codes, and National Insurance codes. In a manual DP system it is not essential or necessarily desirable to code data. A clerk may find it easier to deal with a customer or a supplier or a stock part by name rather than by code number. Furthermore, he or she can cope with variants of names, being able to recognize that

> John Smith
> Smith, John
> Mr John Smith and
> John Smith Esq

all refer to the same individual. A computer, however, will not recognize this, and one advantage of using codes in a computer system is that errors that might arise from ambiguities of this sort are avoided.

A second advantage is the small number of digits in a code number compared to the relatively large number in, say, a customer's name and address. Not only do code numbers reduce the keying-in time, they occupy less computer storage. This can be important when a data entity, such as a customer or a product, is referenced in several files.

There are three types of coding system, employing either purely numeric characters, or purely alphabetic characters, or a mixture of both:

- Numeric codes offer fewer possibilities for a given length of code (only 10 possible characters per space), but they provide for a check digit that can be used to check the accuracy of data entry (see page 198). Examples of numerical coding systems include the ISBN system used to identify books, and the account numbering system used by banks.

- Alphabetic codes offer more possibilities (26 per space), and they can be descriptive. For example, the alphabetic characters used in air-flight codes indicate the destination (LN = London, NY = New York, and so on). However, check digits cannot be used with this type of code.
- Alphanumeric codes offer the most possibilities (36 per space), and can include descriptive alphabetic elements.

## 9.7 Accuracy control

Computers don't make mistakes, and one major advantage of computer data processing over manual methods is the accuracy of the output. However, any errors that creep in when data is input to the system will remain undetected. The constant monitoring of the data by humans which occurs at all stages of manual processing is absent. So in an electronic DP system the whole emphasis of accuracy control is at the data entry stage.

One data entry check that I mentioned above is the check digit that may be appended to a numerical code. This will have a mathematical relationship with the other digits in the number, so that when the number is keyed in the computer checks that the relationship holds. This is an example of *data validation*, a term meaning the process of checking, by means of a computer program, whether data is valid, i.e. permissible. If, in the check digit test, the final digit of the number does not have the required mathematical relationship with the other digits, then the number is invalid.

Data may be valid, but still wrong. It is conceivable that the data entry clerk may incorrectly key two digits of a code number and yet the required mathematical relationship between the digits holds (in other words, a self-cancelling error has occurred). A *data verification* check overcomes this possibility – this checks that the data is correct. Unlike data validation, data verification checks can be expensive, for they usually involve keying in the data twice, first by one data entry clerk and then by another.

Because of the importance attached to the accuracy of

data, data validation and data verification are often applied at the same time.

## 9.8   Data validation methods

1   *Batch total checks.* In this, source documents are assembled in batches at the point at which they are collected, an average batch size being about 20. So clock cards might be batched, invoices batched, and so on.

Attached to the batch will be a *batch control slip*. At the point of collection, a clerk will calculate *batch totals* and write them on the slip. More than one batch total may be calculated. In the case of clock cards, for example, one batch total may be the hours worked as recorded on the cards in the batch, a second may be the sum of the workers' code numbers. In this example, the second total (the sum of the code numbers) has no use or meaning other than its use as a control total, and is called a *hash total*. The first total (the sum of the hours worked) is meaningful: it might, for instance, show the total hours worked in a certain department.

Each batch is passed to the data entry clerk, who keys the data on each document into the system. The clerk also keys in the batch totals, and the computer checks whether these correspond to the totals it works out from the keyed-in numbers. If they do not, it displays a warning message; either a document has gone missing from the batch or been overlooked, or the clerk has keyed in a number incorrectly.

2   *Check digits.* This check is often used with numeric codes. It involves appending to the code number a final digit that has a mathematical relationship with the other digits. The check digit is automatically worked out by the computer and appended when the code number is first created, and then checked each time the code is subsequently keyed in. In one method, the check digit is such that the following relationship holds:

1 × (right-most digit, i.e. the check digit) +
2 × (next digit) +
3 × (next digit) +

4 × (next digit) + . . .
equals a number which is divisible by 11.

Suppose, for example, a code number is 32305. Then X, the check digit that is to be appended, is calculated as shown in Figure 9.2. The result, shown in this figure, is 50 + X, and this must be divisible by 11. Therefore, X must be 5, and the code number with the check digit appended will be 323055.

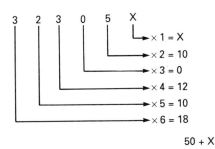

$$50 + X$$

*Figure 9.2*   Check digit calculation

You might like to confirm that the final digit in the ISB number on the back of this book is calculated in this way.

3   *Range check.*   This involves a check by the computer that the data lies within certain limits. In the case of clock card data, for example, the computer might check that the weekly hours worked by an employee are less than 60, and display a warning message if the clerk keys in a number greater than this.

4   *Parity check.*   This is different type of check, applied by the computer to check that errors do not arise during processing. It applies this check each time it moves data around within its store. To each byte that makes up the data, it adds an extra *parity bit*, which will be either a binary 0 or a binary 1 depending on whether the number of 1s in the byte is even or odd. The presence of this bit enables it to check that a bit is not altered when data is moved around. If it is, it repeats the operation. Of course, in the unlikely event of two bits being altered to give a compensating error, this test will fail.

## 9.9   Data verification methods

As we have said, data may be valid and yet wrong. Data verification involves checking that the keyed-in data is actually correct.

1   *Informal check.*   The data entry clerk can informally check the accuracy of his or her work. The computer can assist in this, for in response to keying in the code number of a customer, supplier, or part, for example, it may display the name on the screen.

2   *100% check.*   This is the main type of verification check, and involves keying the data twice, first by one clerk and then by another. The computer checks the second set of entries against the first, and displays a warning message if a discrepancy occurs.

## 9.10   Files

In a computer system, data is stored in *files*. Chapter 6 explained the main computer filing terms and concepts, including *fields* and *records* (see page 130). In data processing systems, there are two kinds of file:

- *Transaction files*, which hold the records of business transactions (such as sales and purchases). The data on these records is called *transaction data*. Such data is added to a transaction file when (or shortly after) the transaction takes place, and it is deleted from the file after the transaction has been processed.
- *Master files*, which hold stock records, employee records, and other non-transaction records. The data on these records, being more permanent than transaction data, is called *standing data*. Some standing data, such as names and code numbers, hardly ever changes, and this is called *reference data*. Other standing data, such as stock balances, may be updated during processing; this is called *master data*.

## 9.11  Processing methods

In DP systems there are two processing methods: *batch* processing and *real-time* processing.

In batch processing, the transaction data is accumulated over the course of several hours onto transaction files and then processed as a batch. This type of processing has the advantage that batch 'runs' can be scheduled for times in the day when the computer is not heavily used, leaving peak periods clear for work that cannot be handled in this way. However, because the transaction data is not processed immediately, this method suffers from the disadvantage that the master data, such as stock balances, are normally slightly out of date.

In real-time processing the computer deals with the transaction data immediately it arises; the data is not first recorded on a transaction file for later processing. Instead, the master file is updated immediately and any transaction documents are produced there and then. However, the data is recorded on a transaction file after the processing has taken place, the sole purpose of this file being to print out an audit trail at the end of the day (see page 217).

Real-time processing has the advantage that the master files are always up to date. The disadvantage is that it makes heavy use of the computer during busy periods. The steadily increasing power of computers is lessening the importance of this disadvantage, with the result that there has been a shift in recent years away from batch processing towards real-time processing.

Batch processing is the traditional way of processing data by computer, involving a large data processing department. Data is sent by the sales, purchasing, and other user departments in the DP department on source documents of various sorts. Working from these, the data entry clerks in the DP department key the data onto transaction files for later processing (see page 209). The output, when it is produced, is dealt with by data control clerks and distributed to the user departments.

Real-time processing, in contrast, passes these tasks over to the user departments. VDUs are installed in the departments, and staff key in the data as it arises and receive an immediate response on their screens. Transaction documents may be printed out immediately on printers in the user departments.

## 9.12 Accessing methods

The process of storing and retrieving data is called *data access*, and a number of data access methods are used in computer systems. Data on transaction files is always accessed in the order in which it was entered into the file, i.e. chronologically. This is called *serial access*. Serial access is similar to sequential access, referred to on page 162: the computer begins at the beginning and reads through and processes each item of data until it reaches the end of the file.

(Note that the term *sequential access* is applied when records are written to and read from the file in key sequence, i.e. code number sequence if the code number is the key. Records on master files are often accessed sequentially. See page 130 for information on key fields.)

Serial and sequential access methods are used in DP applications where all the records in a file have to be accessed. An example in the case of master files is the production of monthly customer statements. Every customer's account details held on the customer file must be looked up in order to produce the statements. If a file is accessed only serially or sequentially, then it can be stored on magnetic tape; this has to be read in sequence from beginning to end, but it is a cheaper form of storage than disk. However, files are often accessed in a random way (see below), and then disk storage is essential.

In many applications, records on master files have to be accessed in a *random* manner. The access device in this case goes straight to the spot on the disk storage device (normally magnetic disk) where the record is held. Invoicing is one example of this: to produce an invoice a particular customer has to be looked up in the customer file, and particular stock lines have to be looked up in the stock file.

A common random access method is *indexed sequential access*. In this, the records are stored in key sequence in the file, with an index which catalogues each record's location and thus allows the computer to find it immediately. In this type of storage method the records can also be read sequentially, if this is necessary.

## 9.13   Data processing activities

Besides processing transaction data, discussed above, there are three other major DP activities: management reports must be produced from the master data on master files, reference data must be kept up to date, and inquiries must be dealt with. Here's a brief account of these activities.

- *Transaction processing.*   This includes the activities you read about in previous sections: recording transaction data on transaction files, updating master data on master files, and printing audit trails. It also includes looking up data on master files in order to process transaction data. To give an example, when a customer's order is processed, the product details (such as the price) must be looked up on the stock file, and these details will be used in the invoice calculations and will ultimately be printed on the invoice and other sales documents.
- *Reporting.*   This is the task of referencing (looking up) data on master files in order to produce management reports. To produce a stock report, for example, every stock record must be looked up in the stock file and the data on those records summarized to produce the various totals required.
- *Enquiries.*   This is the task of looking up data on master files when queries arise. For example, when a sales order arrives it may be necessary to look up the credit status of the customer on the customer file or check the stock balance of an item on the stock file.
- *File maintenance.*   This means keeping the reference data on the master files up to date. Customers' addresses may change, new parts may be added to the stock and other parts deleted, new employees may join the firm and other employees leave. All these changes must be recorded on the files. This is not part of transaction processing (for the changes are not transaction data), but will be done as a special file maintenance job.

## 9.14   Organizing data processing

Data processing in a large organization can be organized in a variety of ways:

- Before the days of computers and other data processing equipment, it was carried out in a *decentralized* way (i.e. in a number of offices in different parts of the organization) using manual methods.
- It has often been carried out in a *centralized* way (i.e. in a central data processing department) using computers. However, with the development of PCs and low-cost terminals, there has in recent years been a shift back towards decentralized DP, though with computers rather than manual equipment.
- Some organizations use the services of an external agency (computer bureau) to process the data.

The sections below analyse each of these ways of organizing DP.

## 9.15   Decentralized DP, using manual methods

This method of processing data is still often used, especially in small organizations. The advantages of this way of processing over traditional data processing centralized on a DP department include:

- Users can access data in their own way and at their own times, instead of having to conform to the requirements of a central facility. So urgent matters and enquiries can be dealt with promptly.
- Users can input data directly into the system instead of filling in and sending source documents to the DP department for input.
- Since the processing facilities are decentralized, it is less likely that a machine breakdown or a strike by a handful of people will disrupt the entire organization.

The disadvantages are mainly that it is a slow, labour-intensive way of processing data, and its accuracy is inferior to that achieved by other methods.

## 9.16 Centralized DP, using computers

Centralized DP came in with the introduction of punched card equipment at the turn of the century. The equipment, although relatively fast and semi-automatic, was very large and very expensive. It therefore had to be offered as a central facility, with user departments sending their data to the new 'data processing department' for processing. Fifty years later the earliest computers, although a significant advance on punched card equipment, were still large and expensive. They also had to be offered as a central facility, thus accelerating the trend towards centralized DP.

With the centralization of DP came batch processing. Punched card equipment was designed to process cards in large batches, and the earliest computers could be operated economically only in this way. The data was keyed on to punched cards using an off-line keypunch (i.e. not connected to the computer, and therefore not drawing on its power), and subsequently read into the system in batches using high-speed on-line card readers.

## 9.17 Decentralized DP, using computers

The advances in computer technology during the last decade have to a large extent reversed this trend towards centralized DP. The emphasis is now once again on decentralized data processing, user departments entering their data and controlling the processing via on-line terminals to the main computer and using networked PCs. Real-time rather than batch processing is normally used, each transaction being entered and processed as it arises, and up-to-date master data being always available for dealing with inquiries.

The reasons for the re-emergence of decentralized data processing include:

- VDUs and PCs are now very cheap, and so can be supplied to user departments.
- Application programs are much more user-friendly than in the past, so can be used by staff who are not DP experts.
- Computers today are very powerful and able to support real-time processing.

## 9.18 Bureau processing

There are a number of computer bureaux offering data processing facilities based on mainframe or minicomputers. The bureau provides the computer hardware and software, the client firm sends in its data for processing. A number of arrangements are possible:

- In one arrangement, the client sends the source documents through the post, the bureau keys it in, processes it, and sends back the output.
- In another, the client keys in the data on a terminal located in the client's premises, and it is sent over the phone line to the bureau's computer, the output being sent back in the same way. Batch processing will be used, as this minimizes both the telephone line time and the computer time.
- In a third, a member of the bureau's staff travels to the client's premises on a periodic basis with a portable computer, and keys in and processes the data on the spot.

The advantages to the client of using a bureau are:

- The client does not face the problems of acquiring and maintaining computer hardware and software. This is particularly useful in the case of specialist computer software which is used only occasionally.
- It provides clients with useful experience of computer processing so that they are better able to make a sensible choice if they eventually decide to acquire their own system.

The disadvantages to the client are:

- If the client is a heavy user of the bureau he/she will face high charges. In these days of low-cost computers these will often compare unfavourably with the house costs of running his/her own system.
- The client will have to adapt his/her DP procedures to conform with the requirements of the bureau's standard application packages.

## 9.19 Multiprogramming

Decentralized data processing and bureau processing involve a number of on-line terminals in user departments or client firms each making simultaneous use of the computer system. To cope with this the computer must have what are called *multiprogramming* capabilities, meaning that it must be able to cope with many users and programs at the same time.

These capabilities are provided by a sophisticated operating system available on mainframe and minicomputers which switches from one terminal and program to another at high speed. This enables the computer to switch from executing a program instruction on one terminal to executing a different program instruction on another, the speed of execution and switching being so fast that the individual user is hardly aware of any delay in the execution of successive processing instructions.

Besides enabling real-time processing, multiprogramming also increases the efficiency of the computer when carrying out batch processing. With single-program execution, one part of the system may be idle while another part is working on its stage of the task; at other times in the program run the situation may be reversed, with the previously idle part busy while other parts are idle. Multiprogramming avoids this. It also allows the computer to carry out batch processing and real-time processing simultaneously.

## 9.20 The data processing department

An organization with a large computer installation will have a data processing department. It may be staffed by systems analysts (who design the computer-based systems), computer programmers (who produce and maintain the programs required by those systems), and computer operations staff (who enter the data and run the programs), all under the control of a data processing manager. A typical organization chart for a DP department is shown in Figure 9.3.

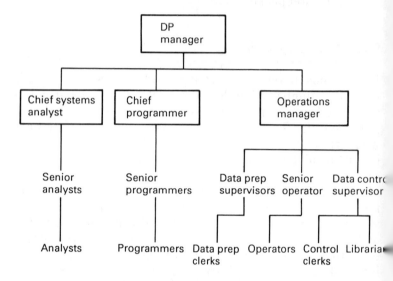

*Figure 9.3*   The data processing department

- *Data processing manager.*   The DP manager has overall responsibility both for the development of new systems and programs and for the day-to-day work of processing the organization's data. In his former role he advises other managers on possible computer applications in their departments and he provides them with analysts and programmers to design and implement those applications. In his latter role he is responsible for ensuring that the computer operations staff input the data accurately, organize the processing efficiently, and pass the output to the users on time.

- *Systems analysts.*   Later in this chapter we shall be looking at the work of systems analysts. Basically, it is to analyse existing systems and design new ones.

- *Programmers.* There are two types of computer programmer:
1 Programmers responsible for systems maintenance. Their job is to maintain (i.e. make changes to or correct) the systems software.
2 Programmers who write and maintain the applications software needed to implement the projects designed by systems analysts.

- *Computer operations staff.* The computer operations section is responsible for any batch processing that has to be done:
1 Receiving, checking, and batching the source documents.
2 Keying in the data on those documents.
3 Getting and loading the programs and files.
4 Running the computer.
5 Distributing the computer output.

These tasks are split amongst the staff of the section, namely the *data control clerks* (who check and batch the source documents, produce the batch totals, and distribute the final output), the *data preparation clerks* (who key in the data), the *librarian* (who looks after the disks and tapes that hold the programs and files), and the *computer operators* who load the disks and tapes and operate the computer so that each job is run at the scheduled time. If a malfunction occurs, it is the operator's responsibility to interpret and act upon the computer error messages. In charge of the section is the *operations manager*, who has to schedule the DP jobs so that the equipment is utilized efficiently.

## 9.21 Systems analysis

In this final part of the chapter we shall be looking mainly at systems analysis. This can be defined as the task of determining the boundaries (i.e. the inputs and outputs) of data processing systems within an organization, and finding out for each system the most cost-effective way of converting the inputs to outputs. As a general rule, systems analysis is conducted with the object of introducing or extending computer processing in the organization.

All commercial organizations have data processing procedures producing transaction documents and management reports, but these procedures do not always work very well. The systems analyst's job is to investigate them and to make recommendations for improvements. We can break down this task into the following main steps:

1 Find out what the outputs of a system should be, i.e. what transaction documents and management reports it should produce. He or she will do this by collecting information on existing procedures by observation and questioning.
2 Decide what data inputs are needed by the system to produce these outputs, i.e. what source documents it needs.
3 Decide how the data inputs should be converted to the required outputs, i.e. what procedures, software, and equipment should be adopted.
4 Compare the benefits that will come from computerizing the system with the costs of computerization, so determining the feasibility or otherwise of the project.

The systems analyst works in an advisory capacity, and has no authority to implement any of the recommendations he may make. It is up to the senior management to decide whether and how to implement, and managers of affected departments will obviously have a major involvement. However, the analyst will normally be closely consulted during the implementation.

## 9.22 The systems project

A major systems project can be broken down into three main phases:

1 The first phase involves deciding whether a computer-based solution to the data processing needs is feasible and cost-effective. This phase is called the *feasibility study*.

2 Assuming that a computer-based solution is feasible, the second phase involves looking at the various subsystems in turn and designing computer-based procedures for each.

3 Once these various subsystems have been computerized, the analyst must bring them together so that they form an integrated whole, drawing upon common files and interrelated procedures. Obviously, the individual subsystems will have been designed with this end in view.

Each one of these phases is a major task, and the whole project may occupy a number of analysts for several years. The next sections examine these phases in more detail.

## 9.23 The feasibility study

This first phase will normally be carried out by a team of staff consisting not only of the systems analyst (or analysts) but staff from the various parts of the organization that will be affected by the changes.

The team will take a global look at the organization, and will attempt to identify possible areas where the computer might be introduced or where its existing use might be extended. Then it will carry out a *cost/benefit analysis* to determine whether computerization is worthwhile. This means that it will attempt to quantify (i.e. express in monetary terms) the overall costs of computerization and the overall benefits to the organization.

The team will present the results of this feasibility study (including the expected costs and benefits) in a *feasibility report*. This will be used by management in deciding whether or not to go ahead with the project. The report will also state what document production, reporting, and enquiry facilities will be needed, and it will recommend suitable equipment.

## 9.24 Computerizing the subsystems

This is the next phase in the systems project. It consists of a number of studies, usually carried out consecutively, covering the various subsystems that were identified in the feasibility report for computerization. The stages of each study are:

1  Problem selection.
2  Terms of reference.
3  Investigation.
4  Analysis.
5  Design.
6  Implementation.

Let's look at each of these stages in turn.

1  *Problem selection.*   This stage will in fact form part of the feasibility study. The principle is that a subsystem should be investigated only if the benefits expected from the investigation are likely to exceed the costs. These costs include the costs of the investigation itself. The analyst will therefore concentrate on systems which have reasonably heavy volumes of routine data processing work, and which therefore offer substantial savings i computerized.

2  *Terms of reference.*   These must be written down before the study of a subsystem begins. They should identif the subsystem and so fix the boundaries of the analyst' investigation. Although he will need to investigate the way in which the subsystem impinges on other subsys tems of the business, he should not, during the curren study, make recommendations for changing thos subsystems.
   The senior management will draw up the terms c reference in consultation with the analyst. They wi normally include a statement setting down in genera terms the benefits expected from the investigation, an an estimate of the expected duration of the investigatio and the number of staff to be allocated to it.

3  *Investigation.*   This stage and the next (the analysi comprise the subsystem feasibility study. Don't confus this with the overall project feasibility study discusse earlier. The purpose of this (subsystem) feasibility stuc

is to identify the ways in which the various procedures within the subsystem might be improved, and to quantify the expected costs of these improvements and the benefits. The cost of running the present system must be compared with the cost of running the proposed system, the cost of change-over must be worked out, and the value of any improvements in, say, management information and customer service must be quantified as accurately as possible.

This investigation involves gathering as much relevant information about the subsystem as possible by questioning managers and staff (using interviews or questionnaire forms), and by tracing the flow of data through the system. The object is to find out what procedures are used, what transaction documents and management reports are produced, and what the volumes of work are, i.e. how many documents of each type are produced each day or week.

4 *Analysis*. The analyst is now in a position to examine critically the existing procedures and outputs of the subsystem. He will attempt to answer the following questions:
- Are managers receiving the reports they need from the subsystem, and are these being produced at the right frequency?
- Can the transaction documents produced by the subsystem be improved – are some unnecessary, should others be introduced, or should they contain more, or less, information?
- How can the procedures be made more efficient?

At this point in his study the analyst must find out the costs and try to quantify anticipated benefits that will arise from any improvements he might make in outputs and procedures. It may not be cost effective to provide all the information needed by managers, and a compromise may have to be worked out. He will eventually arrive at a set of recommendations that he will present to management in a feasibility report. In this he will suggest in outline form the structure of the proposed system, and what transaction documents and reports it should produce. Expected costs and benefits will be quantified and compared. In most cases management will accept his report, with perhaps some amendments.

5   *Design.*   Once management has accepted the feasibility report the analyst can set to work on the design phase of the study. In the case of any procedures which are not to be computerized, this involves revising the manual ways of doing the work, redesigning forms, and producing procedure manuals. For the procedures which are to be computerized, the analyst will need to:

- Design the computer files.
- Design the computer procedures together with input (source) documents and output (transaction) documents and reports.
- Produce a report, called the *systems definition*, which describes the proposed system.

File design includes deciding whether sequential or random access should be employed, as well as determining what fields, field lengths, and coding systems should be used in the records. The analyst must also define how the data is to be input, how the output is to be produced, and any validation and other control procedures.

In the system definition he will give details of every aspect of the proposed system, from specifying how the data is to be input to examples of the transaction documents and reports that are to be produced. He will also describe the computer programs needed.

6   *Implementation.*   The implementation of the proposed system must be comprehensively planned by the systems analyst, and these plans should be included in the system definition. It will involve the following steps.

- Produce documentation describing the new system and how to operate it.
- Retrain the staff, in particular the clerical staff who are to operate the new procedures and equipment.
- Create the master files, by coding the data currently held on manual files and keying it into the system.
- Order the computer stationery.
- Test the new system. Although the individual programs that make up the system will have been tested by the

programmers, there may be errors in the system as a whole. This is best checked by using the new system to process data that has recently been processed by the old system, and comparing the results. Discrepancies must be investigated, and any errors that come to light in the new system must be rectified.

- Run the new system in parallel with the existing system for several weeks, and investigate any further discrepancies that might arise.

## 9.25 Integrating the subsystems

When a number of subsystems have been designed and implemented in this way, the point will be reached when their integration becomes desirable. This involves making arrangements so that subsystems share common computer files, and data is entered into the system only once.

If subsystems are not integrated, then data may have to be entered more than once and stored in more than one file. For example, data on goods received may be entered on the stock file as part of the stock control subsystem, then entered a second time on the supplier file as part of the paying subsystem. This is obviously not a desirable way to run a computer system, though with small-scale microcomputer systems it is sometimes unavoidable.

This phase of the systems project involves:

- Establishing organization-wide coding systems to replace the variety of coding systems that may have developed over the years in the various departments. For example, part numbers in the catalogues produced by the sales department may not match those used in the stores department – this sort of inconsistency must be eliminated.
- Designing procedures so that each subsystem can access data held in the files of another.

## 9.26 Security

Security can be the biggest headache in a large computer system, and the systems analyst must build into his design a number of security procedures. The purpose of these is to protect the files from loss (through fire or other accidents), or theft of data, or unauthorized tampering.

A fire could destroy not just the computer hardware (which is insured and can be fairly easily replaced), but the organization's programs and data files, which may be irreplaceable. Theft may result in competitors getting hold of secret information. Unauthorized tampering with the programs could result in the company being defrauded of large sums of money. The procedures to guard against these are as follows.

1  *Loss through fire or accident.*   The analyst must set up procedures for keeping backup copies of programs and data files on disk or tape to protect against loss. These are called *security copies*. They must be stored in safe locations away from the originals.

   Copies of data files will normally be made at the end of each day. In the event of an accident the current files can be re-created by keying in the day's data again on to the previous day's security copies. The security copy of today's files is called the *father*, and the live files which remain in the system and which are updated by the system during the next day are called the *son*. At the close of the next day a further security copy is made, which becomes the father, the previous father now becoming the *grandfather*. At the end of the following day the grandfather copy is erased and the tape or disk on which it was stored is used to create that day's father, the previous day's father now becoming the grandfather. This son-father-grandfather cycle continues indefinitely. (The reason for *two* backups – father and grandfather – is to guard against the possibility of that both the original and the first backup will be damaged while they are in the same location for the backing-up process, and to guard against corruption in the original being transferred to the backup.)

2  *Theft.*   Attempts may be made to physically steal the disks or tapes containing the organization's data files. This risk is guarded against by restricting access to the computer room and library and by strictly controlling

the movements of disks and tapes between the library and the computer room. More often, theft involves unauthorized personnel copying data by gaining access to the system via a remote terminal. This risk can be guarded against by a number of procedures, including the use of passwords, by restricting access to sensitive files, and by a system that allows only certain terminals with certain electronic 'signatures' to access confidential data. As a number of court cases testify, these procedures do not always work very well, mainly through human carelessness in, for example, the choice of passwords.

3   *Tampering*.   Attempts to defraud companies by tampering with their programs and data files have increased with the increasing use of computers. Owing to the relative lack of human controls in a computer system, this type of risk can be difficult to guard against. The security procedures described above for theft are also relevant for protecting against tampering.

As a check against fraudulent practices, companies are required by law to have their accounts audited. In manual systems the auditors follow an *audit trail*, which means they trace transactions through the system. In a computerized system, however, there may be few documents that can be checked. Furthermore, in such systems any data which is no longer useful may be deleted, which further increases the auditors' problems. The systems analyst may therefore be required to incorporate programs in the system which produce at the end of each day special print-outs of the day's transactions. These form the audit trails that auditors can use to check through transactions.

# 10
# Computer-integrated manufacturing

## 10.1 What is computer-integrated manufacturing?

Computer-integrated manufacturing (CIM) covers a range of technologies and techniques that seek to use the power of the computer to ensure that all activities, equipment, and processes in a manufacturing organization work together in the most effective way to achieve its objectives.

The word 'integrated' means that CIM is more than merely the piecemeal application of the automated production techniques described later in this chapter – robots, NC machines, automatic materials handling, and so on. A central concern is the flow and the use of information, so that each part of the organization, whether sales, purchasing, warehousing, or production, knows at any point in time exactly what it should be doing in order to be properly integrated into other activities and so optimize overall performance. This means that data has to be processed and passed between the various systems and machines, and so CIM is heavily dependent upon data processing.

The technologies and techniques that are embraced by CIM can be split into four broad areas:

- Techniques for planning manufacturing.
- Techniques for controlling manufacturing.
- Techniques for executing manufacturing.
- Techniques for integrating manufacturing.

Some of these techniques are described in this chapter. Here's a comprehensive (though not exhaustive) list of them:

**Techniques for planning manufacturing**

Computer-aided design (CAD)
Computer-aided process planning (CAPP)
Manufacturing resources planning (MRP)
Just-in-time (JIT)
Optimized production technology (OPT)

**Techniques for controlling manufacturing**

Work-in-progress (WIP) planning and control
Automatic materials handling (AMH)
Quality assurance (QA)
Engineering data management (EDM)

**Techniques for executing manufacturing**

CNC (computer-numerically-controlled) machines and robotics
Flexible manufacturing systems (FMS)

**Techniques for integrating manufacturing**

Connectivity issues, including networking standards such as Manufacturing Automation Protocol (MAP).

Note also the following terms:

- CAM (computer-aided manufacture) – used to describe a combination of CNC machines, robots, and automatic materials handling.
- CAD/CAM – used to describe the linking of CAD to CAM, a technique which enables designs created in the drawing office to be passed electronically direct to CNC machines and robots in the factory, which automatically convert them to parts and products.

## 10.2 The evolution of manufacturing technology

The enormous wealth of the industrialized world has been created by the application of technology to manufacturing.

The great evolutionary epochs of the past are well known: the stone age, the iron age, and the age of mechanization (the industrial revolution). Each was the result of a major technological advance, and each has resulted in huge gains in manufacturing productivity and wealth.

We are now into the next epoch, the age of information. The technological advance that ushered in this age (the silicon chip) was described at the start of this book. So far as manufacturing is concerned, the end result of the information revolution will be the appearance of radically new types of factories, and the integration of the whole manufacturing process from the supply of materials and parts to the distribution of the finished goods. The effect of this on society and wealth is difficult to predict, but it will certainly be enormous. (Its impact on employment is discussed in the next chapter.)

The application of computers to manufacturing began around 30 years ago. Since then, there has been a steady evolution in computer-based factory automation techniques, accompanied by a gradual progression towards greater levels of integration. This evolution has, to a large extent, been governed by developments in computers over the last three decades.

*The 1960s.*    Computers were first applied to manufacturing in the early 1960s. These were the days of the early batch-processing mainframe computers, which were suitable for data processing (DP) tasks but not for controlling factory equipment (see later). Consequently it was the DP side of manufacturing that was computerized, the principal technique that we have inherited from that time being MRP.

*The 1970s.*    Then, in the 1970s, new types of computers came along (see page 44). Their significance for manufacturing was that they were able to respond instantaneously to data received from sensors. Individual machines, groups of machines, and processes could now be brought under computer control. However, the lack of standards at this time and the proliferation of differing approaches, meant that these computer-controlled devices were not linked together but worked largely independently of each other. This resulted in the so-called 'islands of automation' (see the next paragraph). During the 1970s, the base technologies of modern manufacturing automation were developed, such as computer-numerically-controlled (CNC) machines and robots, computer-based statistical quality control techniques, and computer-aided design (CAD).

The term 'islands of automation' has been coined to describe the many different computer-controlled devices within a factory that work with little reference to each other, i.e. with no provision for data to pass between them. One example was the use of computers for statistical quality control – these could rapidly signal deviations in the output of a process outside the accepted tolerance limits, but they could not stop the process for the fault to be rectified. This meant that the overall control and coordination of the process was carried on much as before, i.e. by manual rather than electronic methods.

As indicated above, this lack of communication between automated equipment was due to the lack of agreed standards, rather than being an inherently difficult task. Indeed, while the physical work that lathes and millers (for instance) might do is different, the task of controlling them is actually very similar, using devices called programmable logic controllers (PLCs).

*The 1980s.* The 1980s has been the decade of the personal computer and computer networks. It is the latter that has been particularly significant for manufacturing, for it has enabled many different computers and pieces of equipment to be linked together electronically. ('Connectivity' is the term that's often used to describe this.) This is bringing about the next phase of the evolution in factory automation, namely the setting up of connections between the islands of automation, and between these islands and a supervisory computer. A demonstration of this is the linking of CAD systems to manufacturing systems, so that designs produced in the drawing office are sent electronically to the factory machines, where, with the minimum of human intervention, they are converted to products. This linkage leads to further productivity and performance gains. It also allows the power of the computer to be used to integrate the various processes, ensuring that they work together to optimize the performance of the enterprise as a whole. The term computer-integrated manufacturing (CIM) is specifically applied to this development.

*The 1990s.* It looks like the 1990s will be the age of telecommunications, resulting in connectivity not just within an organization but between organizations. An example of the trend towards this is the growing number of companies communicating with each other using Electronic Data Interchange (EDI) technology (see page 191). EDI allows standard electronic 'forms' – such as purchase orders or invoices – to be passed between the computers of different organizations, cutting out postal delays and saving storage space and paperwork handling costs.

This type of development will lead to the integration of factory systems with the systems of outside suppliers and customers. Some organizations are already moving in this direction, prompted mainly by the development of just-in-time (JIT) techniques, which aim to cut inventories and improve efficiency by ensuring that supplies of materials and parts arrive at the point of production immediately prior to manufacturing. The successful application of JIT depends partly on the supplier of materials and parts responding rapidly to a customer's requirements, which in turn depends upon his manufacturing and distribution systems receiving timely data via EDI from the customer's manufacturing systems. This is best achieved by electronic links between the computers of the two organizations, and from there it is but a short step to arranging that the supplier's factory responds automatically to demands from the customer's factory.

Another result of the development of telecommunications is the concept of the 'global shop floor'. Many organizations have geographically-dispersed factories, with different parts of the production process carried out in different countries and so they need to apply CIM concepts across national frontiers. Groups of machines need to be linked not just to other equipment in their own factory but to equipment in other factories in the organization. The systems that have evolved track work-in-progress (WIP) not just in the individual factory but throughout the entire organization.

## 10.3   The impact of CIM

There are, as yet, no factories which are integrated to the extent that all operations – from order to processing through design and manufacture to distribution – are centrally controlled and coordinated by computer. Indeed, in many cases it is not desirable to aim for such a high level of integration and automation. Where factory automation has been applied, the aim so far has been to integrate some parts only of the enterprise. Here are three examples:

- In one organization, CAD/CAM might be applied. This integrates and automates the design and manufacturing processes, but it impinges only marginally on other areas.
- In another organization, JIT might be applied. This integrates manufacturing and distribution, but has limited impact elsewhere.
- Yet another organization might apply both CAD/CAM and JIT. Although this extends the degree of integration, there are many activities still excluded.

## 10.4   DP and CIM

Traditionally, data processing (DP) has impacted mainly the business operations area, being concerned with the automation of order processing, stock control, and accounts. However, with the replacement of islands of automation by CIM, DP has come to play a crucial role in engineering operations and production as well.

A very simplistic view of how DP and factory automation work together is shown in Figure 10.1. Customer orders are input to the DP system, one output being the production plans which tell the CAM system in the factory what to make. Another output from the DP system is reports that analyse sales and customer preferences, which can be used by the design function as a basis for product improvements. The designs, created on the CAD system, are passed to the CAM system, where they are converted into finished products.

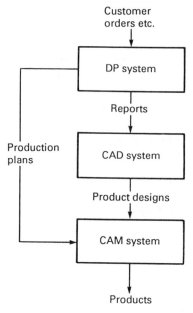

*Figure 10.1*  The interaction of DP and factory automation systems

## 10.5  The benefits of factory automation

Organizations which have implemented CIM techniques have benefitted in a number of ways. A recent survey commissioned by the DTI and carried out by Benchmark Research revealed the following perceived benefits from CIM:

- Increased flexibility in manufacturing operations.
- Increased productivity.
- Reduction in lead times.
- Reduction in costs.
- Improved product quality.

## 10.6  Creating the integrated factory

To implement CIM, the DP system and the various automated manufacturing systems (see page 219) must be closely tied together by electronic links. There must be a large computer (typically a mainframe) in overall control of these systems, running special software such as the TIME software described in the next section. This same computer may also run the DP system and the various CIM systems, in which case the links between these systems will be purely software links.

The first phase may be to link the CAD system to the CAM system, to create a CAD/CAM system. In this, the product design created on the CAD software is converted by the CAM software to instructions for the factory machines, so that the settings for the machines and the tools used are automatically determined.

In the second phase, the DP system may be tied to the CAD/CAM system to create what's sometimes called an *integrated factory*. In this, the information from customers' orders is used to control the scheduling and loading of work in the factory, so that it automatically produces what's required. As well as this, the DP system is linked to the CAD system, so that it passes to management reports and market information for use in product design.

These key systems that make up the integrated factory are shown in Figure 10.1. Note that the links that are shown in the diagram between these systems take place via the controlling software, as explained in the next section.

At present, CAD/CAM is quite widely employed, but few integrated factories exist, apart from some in Japan.

The remaining sections of this chapter describe a range of CIM technologies and techniques, beginning with a brief description of software that can be used to control the integrated factory.

## 10.7 Controlling the integrated factory

One example of software for controlling the integrated factory is *TIME*, short for Tandem Integrated Manufacturing Environment. As its name implies, this system is a product of Tandem Computers, and runs on their mainframes.

A schematic of the TIME system is shown in Figure 10.2. It consists of three modules, called *Factory Manager*, *Document Manager*, and *Device Manager*. These modules perform the following broad tasks:

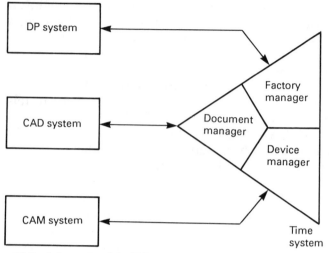

*Figure 10.2*    Schematic of the TIME system

- The Factory Manager controls the minute-by-minute progress of parts through the factory, to ensure that orders are produced at the right time and to the right specifications. The basis of this control is information on customer orders obtained from the DP system.
- The Document Manager takes the designs produced by the CAD system and passes them around the factory to the machines that require them, when they require them.
- The Device Manager is really the interface between these two managers and the factory machines. It interprets the information produced by the Factory Manager and the Document Manager into the instructions that are passed to the CNC machines, robots, and other factory devices.

The following sections describe four of the main CIM techniques, namely MRP, CAD, CAM, and FMS.

## 10.8   Manufacturing resources planning

Manufacturing resources planning (MRP) was one of the first attempts to use computers to aid manufacturing. It

originated in the 1960s under the name 'material requirements planning', and it used the data processing computers
of the day to speed up the main aspects of a manufacturer's
pre-production paperwork:

- Generating purchase orders for the supply of raw
  materials and parts required by the manufacturing
  process.
- Generating works orders instructing the workshops to
  carry out manufacturing operations to meet orders.

To generate these outputs, the computer requires information from the following sources:

- The manufacturing schedule, i.e. the long-term production plan which specifies what finished products have to
  be produced by what dates. The finished product
  demand is expressed in numbers of units, while the due
  date is expressed as a period number.
- The bill of materials, which describes the relationship
  between the finished product and the parts and assem-
  blies that make it up.
- The inventory records, which show the current balances
  of the parts in stock.

In addition, the computer needs to know the lead times for
purchasing raw materials and parts, and also the manufacturing lead times for any made-in parts. The former will
usually be held on the inventory records, while the latter
will be held on the bill of materials file.

The computer then goes through a process described as a
time-phased gross to net explosion'. This rather colourful –
if somewhat confusing – expression means that the
computer:

1. Compares the products specified in the manufacturing
   schedule with the information in the bill of materials to
   work out the quantities of parts required.
2. Uses the lead times to calculate the due dates.
3. From the current stock position calculates what quantities are required to be manufactured or purchased.

In the late 1970s MRP was further developed and renamed 'manufacturing resource planning'. It now became an all-embracing system covering the entire manufacturing planning process, particularly the financial aspects. This means that important factors could be taken into account which were previously ignored, such as the effect of cash flow on the manufacturing plan. For the first time the manufacturing side of the enterprise was integrated with the financial side, and MRP was able to develop a company-wide business plan.

Since the 1970s, the main advances in this technique have been:

- The reduction in the size and cost of computers, so that quite small manufacturing companies can now apply MRP.
- The adoption of interactive processing using on-line terminals, so that staff in production departments can enter data directly into the system and receive instantaneous responses. This means that they have an up-to-date picture instead of one which may be a week or more out of date.

## 10.9    Computer-aided design

A computer-aided design (CAD) package uses the power of the computer to do for drawings what a word processing package does for text. After MRP, it was the second main way in which IT revolutionized the production process.

Like WP, CAD enables you to:

- Delete, insert, copy, and move things rapidly and easily around on the computer screen.
- Insert existing material stored on disk – such as drawings of parts of sub-assemblies – into your latest masterpiece so that you are not constantly re-inventing (or rather re-drawing) the wheel.
- Format your work, so that it is printed or plotted in the colours, line types and so on, that you require.

CAD packages also offer a number of additional and valuable drawing aids:

- The computer's equivalent of geometric tools such as the compass, the ruler, the protractor, and arcs.
- The computer's equivalent of the nib, that allows you to draw different types of thicknesses of lines.
- A grid, so that the start and end points of any lines that you draw are locked onto a grid of 'graph paper' points on the screen.
- Zoom facilities, enabling you to expand any part of your drawing on the screen and thereby work more accurately.
- Rotating, inverting, and other facilities enabling you to manipulate parts of your drawing in a very flexible way.
- Scaling facilities, enabling you to type in line lengths, angles, and other dimensions at the keyboard, the computer converting these to the required lines on the screen.
- Dimensioning facilities, which automatically calculate and display on your drawing the lengths of any lines that you may have drawn.

The keyboard is not a suitable drawing tool, and so CAD systems normally use a mouse or similar device.

CAD systems can achieve impressive productivity gains in drawing offices, and it is often claimed that a 400% increase in output can be achieved. This does, however, assume that the draftsman is familiar with the CAD system and is using its capabilities to the full.

To give an example of the speed at which an item can be drawn, consider a spoked wheel. To draw this, it is only necessary to draw a single spoke and then rotate it through 360 degrees about the centre point of the wheel, duplicating the spoke say every 15 degrees. The hub and the rim can then be rapidly drawn using the CAD package's electronic compass. Any bolts or other parts can be called up from a library held on disk and inserted as required on the drawing.

Even greater productivity can be achieved when the CAD system is linked directly to the CAM system, described below. Then, the CAD data can be used directly to control the settings of automatic machines in the factory.

## 10.10   Computer-aided manufacture

Computer-aided manufacture (CAM) refers to the use of computers to control the manufacturing process, primarily by controlling the settings of tools and the way they are used in computer-numerically-controlled (CNC) machines and other automatic devices, and by controlling the deployment of industrial robots. The CAM system uses the production plans produced by the DP system, and the product designs produced by the CAD system, to work out what should be made at what times and on which machines.

To understand what's involved, you should know that factory production typically involves two major processes:

- The machining of parts
- The handling of parts and their assembly.

Today, CNC machines can carry out the first process very efficiently, even for small runs. Operating automatically under software instructions, they can apply various drilling, turning, and cutting devices to the raw material to manufacture an accurately-made part.

Robots can carry out the second of these processes, for they can handle materials and feed them to the CNC machines. They can also remove the finished parts and, if necessary, assemble them to make the finished products. Like CNC machines, they can be used economically for small runs. An industrial robot typically consists of a *robot arm* with a clasping device or other tools attached.

Early generations of CNC machines and robots lacked 'intelligence', meaning that they did not have sensor devices enabling them to respond to changes in their environment. In the case of robots, this meant that they would perform the sequence of operations dictated by the controlling software, blindly picking up and manipulating whatever object happened to be placed in the operating position, or, if nothing was there, picking up and manipulating empty space.

Modern generations of CNC machines and robots are equipped with sensors enabling them to identify and locate objects, and so make adjustments to the programmed sequence of operations that they have to perform. In essence, a machine of this type consists of three systems:

- A mechanical system to operate tools or to pick up and manipulate objects. This system may include rotating shafts, drills, and other tools, as well as clasping and other handling devices.
- A sensory system to detect what the mechanical system is doing and, in the case of robots, to identify and locate objects. A variety of sensing devices are used, including, for robots, video 'eyes'.
- A control system which interprets the information received by the sensory system and uses it to control the mechanical system. This system is normally based on microchips.

In simple terms, the sequence of operations that takes place when one of these machines performs a task is as follows:

- The sensory system converts the position of a part into data in the form of an electrical signal.
- The control system compares this with an ideal computed position based on data from the controlling program.
- The difference between the two is the 'error', and is represented by tiny digital pulses of electricity.
- These pulses are fed to the mechanical system, where they are converted to analogue form, and amplified to the level needed to adjust the positions of the arms and tools.

In a CAM system, a production line consists of CNC machines, robot arms, and materials transfer systems, all under the control of a central computer.

## 10.11 Flexible manufacturing systems

Because modern CNC machines and robots are software-driven, they can be switched from task to task in a very flexible way. Also, production plans can be equally flexible, because they are calculated by the computer data processing system. The combination of the two is *flexible manufacturing systems* (FMS), a term used to describe the ability of modern manufacturing operations to switch rapidly from one product specification to another.

FMS offers great benefits for many types of production:

- Batch production, which accounts for a large part of manufacturing activity, can be automated, with resulting cost and quality benefits.
- Large-scale production is no longer tied to huge production runs of identical products. A car manufacturing plant, for example, can make cars to order without incurring heavy set-up costs. This means that dealers or customers can specify the colours and accessories required, and the quantities, and these can be quickly assembled.
- FMS allows the factory to operate on a just-in-time (JIT) basis, i.e. parts and products can be made at the time that they are required, rather than being made for stock weeks or months ahead. This cuts down greatly on stockholding costs.

# 11
# IT and society

## 11.1 Introduction

Most of this book has concentrated on the technology of information processing and its business applications. This final chapter covers its impact on society in general.

- We look at its impact on work and employment. Here, IT is changing the content of jobs. Old skills and practices are disappearing, and new ones emerging. New machines and new products are developed at an ever-increasing rate, creating new markets and jobs, while companies and industries that stick with old technology decline, shedding jobs.
- Turning to education and training, we see that computer-based training is steadily encroaching on traditional methods.
- We look also at the impact of IT on commerce, including retailing and banking. 'Intelligent' cash cards are making their appearance, and supermarket point-of-sale terminals that analyse our purchases, update the store's records, and even dispense cash from our bank accounts are now part of the everyday shopping scene.
- We consider too its impact on the home. Here, the microchip is used in more and more appliances. We read of the 'intelligent home', in which the central heating system, the burglar alarm, the cooker, the video, and other systems are all linked into and controlled by a computer.
- Further examples of the way IT impacts society at large can be seen in the growing use of computers in all aspects of public administration and national defence.

The Gulf War graphically illustrated the devastating effect of computers applied to battle control systems and guided bombs. We consider at the end of this chapter the impact of IT on personal privacy and national security.

## 11.2  IT and employment

The IT revolution is just the latest in a long line of technological revolutions: the stone age, the bronze age, the iron age, and so on. All these technological advances have had two main effects upon employment:

- They have altered the pattern of employment, as old skills and jobs become obsolete and new ones emerge. During this transition period, inevitable social dislocations arise.
- They have resulted in increased productivity, so that more is produced for the same amount of labour. This has led to increased wealth, to the ability of society to support jobs that are not concerned with the direct production of food and other material products, and also to increased leisure. The increased leisure may express itself as shorter working hours, or actual unemployment. (In earlier times this unemployment manifested itself in the rise of the 'leisured classes'. Only in recent times has it resulted in 'working class' unemployment.)

The technological advances that have occurred in the last couple of centuries (i.e. since the start of the industrial revolution) differ from earlier advances in two important respects:

- They have happened very rapidly, so that the social dislocations have been more acute. Large numbers of people can be thrown out of work in the space of only a few years. And people with jobs need significant amounts of retraining several times in their working lives.
- They involved a heavy investment in manufacturing

plant. This has led, in the initial phase of the advance, to a significant increase in employment.

The current technological advance is based upon the widespread adoption of the microchip in manufacturing plant and in manufactured products. The various elements of computer-integrated manufacturing technology are appearing – robots, automatic materials handling, CAD/CAM, and so on (see Chapter 10). The investment in this technology should result in a significant increase in both output and employment in the industrialized world in the short term as new kinds of machines and new kinds of factories are developed and constructed. The long-term effects may be static or declining employment.

One of the features of technological advance is the changing employment patterns and the need for new skills. This is manifesting itself at present by the concern being expressed by many industries in many parts of the developed world at the shortage of suitably trained and skilled labour.

## 11.3   IT and employment patterns

As I've said, one of the effects of technological advance is increased productivity and greater wealth. This reduces the labour required for the production of food and for other basic economic tasks, and increases the ability of society to sustain other types of jobs. So, over the centuries, we have seen a steady movement of labour away from agriculture, mining, and other 'primary' industries, through 'secondary' (i.e. manufacturing) industries, and into the 'tertiary' (service industry) sector of the economy.

- A few centuries ago most of the labour force worked in primary sector, on the land. Today, the figure is one or two percent.
- A few decades ago, most of the labour force was employed in manufacturing.
- Today, most of the labour force works in service industries.

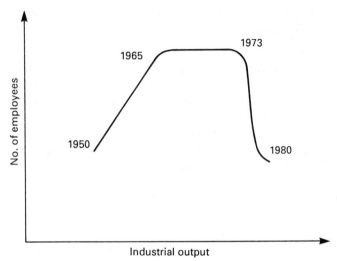

*Figure 11.1*　Employment and output, 1950 to 1980

This steady movement in the pattern of employment is likely to continue, and even accelerate with the introduction of computer-integrated manufacturing. It may be that in two decades from now manufacturing employment will fall to the kinds of levels that we associate with farming, with perhaps 95% of jobs being in the service sector. Many people in the service sector are 'information' workers, using IT equipment such as computers to process their work.

One of the features that characterized the industrial revolution was the concentration of manufacturing in factories with expensive large-scale plant and production lines. So there was a mass movement of people away from the countryside into the towns and cities where the factories were concentrated. Although the industrial revolution raised living standards enormously, this mass migration to urban areas lowered the quality of many aspects of people's lives. In contrast to this, the information technology revolution is characterized by the miniaturization of computer components and the development of communications networks. As a result, the need for information workers to travel to work in large city offices is reduced. Many jobs can be done in remote locations, linked electronically to the central site. So many companies are moving their offices away from congested centres of population, and a number of individuals now carry out a significant part of their work on personal computers at home, able to communicate with their organization's central computer via the telephone network. This reverses some of the negative influences of the industrial revolution, leading to improvements in the quality of life.

## 11.4   IT and job content

We've examined the likely impact of IT on employment numbers, and on the kinds of jobs that are going to be available in future. But what will those jobs be like? Will they be monotonous jobs requiring few skills, involving perhaps the repetitive input of data on a computer terminal? Or will the computer itself do all the boring bits, leaving human workers to concentrate on the creative, problem-solving side?

Let's examine what's happened in the past as a result of technological advances. Some jobs have indeed been de-skilled, and become extremely monotonous. One only has to compare the kind of jobs that are done in a furniture factory today with the work of master craftsmen in the past to realize that this is the case. Other jobs have become much more interesting, as computers have enabled people to take on a wider range of responsibilities and acquire a wider repertoire of skills.

In fact, just as the new technology can improve the general quality of life (see last section), so it is able to improve the general quality of jobs. If, in an organization, jobs are mostly negatively affected by the introduction of new technology, then this is probably the fault of the way in which the technology has been applied, not of the technology itself. *Job design* is the name of the game, and organizations that apply it improve not only the quality of jobs, but also the morale of staff, and the levels of motivation and commitment.

Many jobs in factories and offices are based upon the *production-line* approach to work. In this, the tasks are split into small elements, and each worker undertakes just a few of those elements. This is also called the *scientific* approach to work, as it can result in high levels of efficiency; workers do not spend time moving from one task to another, training needs are minimal, and so on. The cost, though, is reduced morale, alienation of the worker from his/her work, and so on.

Job design aims to improve the quality of jobs by adopting what's called the *whole-task* approach. In this, each worker carries out every part of a task. This is not as technically efficient as the scientific approach, and it requires more training, but the benefits of increased motivation etc. may outweigh this. Certainly, it is a more humane way of organizing the work force.

To compare the two approaches, imagine a small sales office. Under the production-line approach, one person may be responsible for taking all the orders, another may be responsible for all the invoicing, a third may be responsible for ensuring orders are filled, and so on. Under the whole-task approach, one person may be responsible for all these tasks for a customer of a certain type or located in a certain geographical area, another may cover the full range of tasks for a second group of customers, and so on. That way, each member of staff can become familiar with the needs of his/her customers, is fully responsible for ensuring the customer receives his order and is properly invoiced, etc. And although more training is required, the benefit is that one person can look after another's job in an emergency, and staff acquire a wider range of skills and so are more suitable material for promotion.

The computer and other automatic equipment accentuate the effects of these two approaches. If tasks are broken down on a production-line basis, the computer will reduce the range of operations that have to be performed still further. If the whole-task approach is adopted, the computer, by automating the mindless parts of the task, can have the effect of allowing the job to encompass an even greater range of responsibilities.

## 11.5  IT and training

Technological advances demand an increasingly well-educated work force. As we've said, jobs may require a wider range of skills than ever before, and the rate at which they change and progress requires a greater sophistication and flexibility. Training is becoming an increasingly important element, and most workers will require retraining several times in their working lives, as old jobs disappear and new ones emerge.

Traditional education and training courses, in institutions such as colleges of further and higher education, aim to meet this need. However, they have some drawbacks:

- There are too few courses available, owing to the high cost of laying them on. A typical figure for a college course is £20 per student-hour.
- Many potential students are not able to attend the courses that are provided, either because they live too far away, or because the courses are held at times that are not convenient to them.
- Many feel apprehensive about returning to a classroom situation after years away from a formal teaching environment.

IT offers a solution to this in the form of *computer-based training* (CBT). With this, costs can be as low as £2 per student-hour, the materials can be available at places and times that suit the individual student. Many CBT courses can be taken at home. Increasingly, the materials are becoming available over telecommunications networks, and students can get in touch with tutors by the same means. The extension of the optical fibre network and other broad-band telecommuications links such as satellite will facilitate this. For example, the Europa satellite broadcasts several hours a day of educational and training materials.

Besides these economic advantages, well-designed CBT material can give much better results in terms of improved learning and understanding.

- Because a CBT lesson can be taken by hundreds or thousands of students, much more effort can be put into its production than can be justified for a teacher-centred lesson aimed at 20 or 30 people.
- Modern technology allows the designer of the material

to apply the most effective type of presentation, whether text, image, audio, etc.

- The interactive nature of the technology enables the learner to take his own route through the material, and to instantly check his understanding.

CBT material will often use a multimedia approach, and may incorporate interactive video (see page 164). It will certainly include computer software and lesson material, as well as some material in printed form (if only to explain how to use the system).

It will consist of a number of computer-based lessons, each one lasting, typically, between 15 and 20 minutes. A lesson may be broken into several learning episodes, each of which consists of:

- The learning material, which may take the form of text and graphics displayed on the computer screen or presented via some other medium.
- Questions on the learning material, which are displayed on the screen and which the learner has to answer by typing at the keyboard.
- Feedback displayed on the computer screen, telling the learner whether he or she has answered correctly and giving help and further information if required.
- Scoring, meaning that the computer gives marks according to the correctness or otherwise of the learner's responses, and stores them so that the learner and the tutor can assess performance.
- Branching, meaning (a) that the computer routes the learner through the lesson material on the basis of performance (so that, for example, learners exhibiting poor performance re-do the lesson or are routed to appropriate remedial material); and (b) that the learner is able to exercise some degree of control over his route through the material, by being presented with choices at appropriate points.

CBT is normally produced using a special kind of computer programming language called an *authoring language* (see page 164). This provides facilities for:

- Entering text for displaying on the computer screen.
- Matching the learner's responses to questions against those anticipated by the author.
- Scoring.
- Branching.

Even with these and other software tools, producing CBT is a time-consuming and skilled task. It often involves subject-matter experts, writers, programmers, and possibly other media specialists such as graphic designers. Typically, one hour of learner material takes between 30 and 100 hours to produce. The pay-off is that, like a book, the material can be used over and over again by a large number of people, resulting in a low cost per student-hour.

## 11.6   IT and the high street

IT has brought about a consumer revolution. Cash is giving way to plastic cards; electronic point-of-sale terminals linked to the store's ordering system and to the banking system are appearing everywhere; and shopping and banking can even be done from a home computer linked to the telephone network.

Plastic money is of two types:

- Credit cards, such as Access and Visa, which allow you to purchase goods without the need to make an immediate payment. Stores can add a small surcharge to your bill if you use this payment method, and the credit card company will charge you interest if you don't settle your account by the due date.
- Debit cards, such as Switch and Link, which also allow you to purchase goods by directly debiting your bank account. Many debit cards double up as cash cards, allowing you to draw cash from your bank account. This gives an instant and cost-free way of getting at your money via *automatic telling machines* (ATMs) at any participating branch, not only in this country but in many other countries also. (Switch cards can be used at many banks in a number of European countries; Link – also known as 'Plus' – cards can be used in America.)

Plastic money is becoming 'smart', through the incorporation of a microchip in the card. Smart cards are widely used in a number of European countries, in Japan, and in America, both as store credit cards and as bank debit/cash cards. The phonecard introduced in this country by British Telecom is an example of a smart card.

The RAM in a smart card is able to hold up to 1 million characters, and can store details of the customer's transactions. Since this information is held in the card itself, it avoids the need to access the central computer to check the customer's account each time a transaction is made, so cutting down on computer costs and telecommunications costs. In the case of store cards or bank cards, it is necessary to periodically update the computer by reading out the data from the card via a terminal.

IT is also revolutionizing point-of-sale terminals in supermarkets and other large stores. Electronic point-of-sale (EPOS) terminals offer many facilities, including, through their links to the banking system, debit/cash card facilities. They can:

- Read the bar code printed on the packaging of a product, and so identify it.
- Match this identity with the product's description and price held in its store.
- Store the transaction details, along with information such as the time of the transaction, the method of payment, and the sales assistant's code number.
- Produce fully itemized receipts.
- Update the store's inventory records.
- Accept debit cards as a payment method, and even act as a cash point, dispensing cash.
- Produce data, if required, on the sales assistant's rate of work.

## 11.7   IT and the home

If we include TV and audio technology within the scope of IT, then IT has already revolutionized much of our home lives. Besides giving us access to ordinary TV programs, most new TV sets also offer teletext facilities, allowing us to access the Ceefax and Oracle databases. Further advances in the use of IT in the home will lie mainly in the introduction of the microchip into ever more appliances, the linking of those appliances to a central home computer, and the linking of that computer to the telecommunications network.

Home banking and home shopping have been available for almost a decade via a computer connected to the telephone network. The computer I am using to write this book is also my personal banking terminal. When I type in a simple command, the computer automatically runs a communications software package and then proceeds to carry out the following actions:

- It dials up Prestel (using its internal modem) and logs on with my Prestel account number and passwork.
- It routes me to the Homelink banking section of Prestel.
- It logs on to my Homelink account with my account number and password.

All I have to do is type in a security 'transaction number', and my bank statement appears on the computer screen. Then I can pay bills such as my quarterly electricity or gas charges, or Visa card payments, simply by typing in the appropriate details. The Homelink computer lets me specify the dates when the bills are to be paid, so that I can earn maximum interest on my money. And I can transfer funds between my Homelink account and my ordinary bank account.

Bringing the various microchip-controlled home appliances under the computer's supervision is already technically feasible, and Thorn EMI has built a prototype 'intelligent home'. Figure 11.2 illustrates the electronic links between the various systems. The kind of scenario that is envisaged is as follows:

Returning from a family outing you are delayed by a traffic jam caused by a motorway accident, which means you will be late home. The house is empty. Your meal, which is in the oven set to cook on automatic, will be cold by the time you arrive; the central heating timer

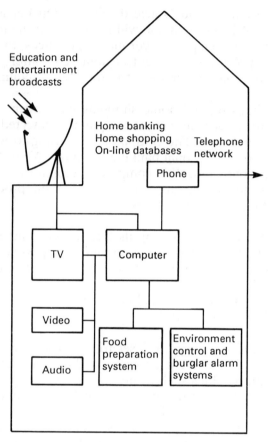

*Figure 11.2*　The intelligent home

will switch the heating on unnecessarily early; you will miss the final episode of the TV serial you have been watching; and with night falling, the house will be in total darkness with the curtains open, an attractive target for burglars.

Your home and its appliances are, however, under the control of your computer. By phoning home you can access this system, and so re-program the oven, reset the central heating system, set the video recorder, close the curtains, check that the burglar alarm system is on, and switch on the lights in a predetermined sequence to simulate people at home.

## 11.8 IT and the arts

During the past half century or so, technology has revolutionized communications media, bringing into being radio, cinema, television, records, and audio and video cassettes. Each one of these forms of communication has had a considerable and obvious impact on the arts. Not only have they made the major forms of art universally and freely available, they have profoundly influenced the art forms themselves. Radio drama, for instance, is a quite new art form, as is much of the art of the cinema.

Today, the main thrust of information technology is centred on computers, and the present generation of computers with their graphics and multimedia capabilities are having a major impact on the production of works of art. We can summarize their influence as:

- Increasing the tools available to the artist, so offering him a new range of artistic possibilities. Electronic music is one obvious example of this.
- Increasing the productivity of the artist, so enabling him to work more quickly. Modern computer animation techniques provide an example of this. To produce an animated cartoon, the artist need only draw a relatively small number of key frames, for the computer is able to construct the intermediate ones (see page 162).

Computers are now being applied to all the main forms of art.

1 *Music.* Hardware and software for the production of synthesized music are important applications of computers, providing features such as a wide range of musical sounds and effects, the ability to instantly alter, in a composition, musical variables such as pitch, tempo, loudness, and the automatic generation and printing of sheet music for music composed directly on the keyboard.

2 *Animation and visual effects.* Computer animation, which made possible a number of films such as Star Wars and its sequels, is now becoming an art form in its own right, and a number of short films made entirely by com-

puter have now been released. Computer graphics, video titling, and other computer-based techniques are also being widely used in TV and video production.

3   *Writing.*   Computer software is available for expressing a writer's prose in crisp, straightforward English. You can, for example, process paragraphs taken from the works of Dickens with this software, with remarkably effective results. At a more mundane level, electronic thesauruses are now included with many word processing packages.

4   *Games.*   The computer game, especially the adventure game, is becoming a quite new form of art. The more sophisticated games incorporate the most impressive computer graphics, and the quality of the synthesized music that is used with some of them is also impressive.

The application of computers to the arts can only grow in the future, not only in the areas listed above but in quite new areas also. For example, 3-D modelling on computers may be applied to sculpture and other solid-object art forms, and some attempts have already been made to use computers to aid the production of poetry.

## 11.9   IT and privacy

In all countries there is a conflict between the need on the one hand to maintain public records and public order, and the need on the other to maintain personal freedom, on the other. We all desire efficient public administration and policing, but few of us relish the infringement of personal liberties that may result. The problem is becoming increasingly acute as the information processing capabilities available to government bodies and the police become ever more sophisticated. They include such things as:

- The on-line retrieval of information on all citizens from a variety of government and business databanks, such as those held on Social Security and Inland Revenue computers.
- Developments in personal movement monitoring, such

as car recognition systems which, if installed on highways, could allow the police to track any vehicle.

In order to safeguard personal freedoms, the EC has laid down codes of practice regarding the storage and retrieval of personal data on electronic systems. In this country, these principles are embodied in the Data Protection Act 1984.

The main aim of this Act is stated by the Data Registrar to be to meet the concern 'arising from the threat which mis-use of the power of computing equipment might pose to individuals. This concern derives from the ability of computing systems to store vast amounts of data, to manipulate data at high speed and, with associated communications systems, to give access to data from locations far from the site where the data are stored.' (Data Protection Act Guideline No. 1.)

The main provisions of the Act are that all public and private organizations which hold data about individuals or companies on computer systems must register this fact with the Data Registrar, and they must register the purpose for which the data is held. The data must not be used for any other purpose, nor may it be disclosed to other bodies. Furthermore, anyone can find out from the Registrar whether an organization holds data about him, and he can obtain a copy of that data.

In detail, the Act covers what it calls 'data users' and 'data subjects'. It defines data users as 'organizations or individuals who control the contents and use of a collection of personal data, processed, or intending to be processed, automatically'. A data subject is 'an individual to whom personal data relate'. Data users must register the personal data they hold, and how they use it, obtain it, and disclose it.

The Act states that personal data must be:

- Obtained and processed fairly and lawfully.
- Held and used only for the specified purposes.
- Adequate, relevant, and not excessive to those purposes.
- Accurate and kept up to date.
- Deleted when it is no longer needed for the specified purposes.

- Stored in a system with security measures taken against unauthorized access, alteration, or destruction of the data.

There are some exceptions to the Act. These include personal data held for managing household affairs or for recreational purposes. So there is no need for you to register names and addresses of friends that you hold for your personal use on your home computer.

## 11.10   IT and national security

Two of the problems that organizations face when they computerize are:

- Increased vulnerability to machine breakdown.
- Risk of unauthorized users tampering with their data.

Because, after computerization, all major functions tend to be centred on the computer, the consequences of both can be disastrous. So organizations go to great lengths to guard against these possibilities, with expensive maintenance contracts, back-up procedures, and elaborate password and other security devices. In spite of this, computers still go wrong, hackers are still able to break into systems, and the extent of computer fraud, although unknown, is large. When public administration and national defence operations are computerized, however, the dire consequences of a malfunction or unauthorized access are magnified many times.

As I write this, the United States National Research Council has just published a report on computer security called Computers at Risk (published by the National Academy Press, Washington). It states that the computer 'will replace the bomb as a terror weapon', and that attacks on national and private computers could cost lives, disrupt banking and commerce, and corrupt important national data. It states that with increasing computerization and networking, these risks will increase rapidly.

Apart from these terrorist risks, over-dependence upon electronic systems can be very dangerous in time of war.

For example, a special type of nuclear device, detonated high in the atmosphere, could release a short burst of high-energy radiation which would knock out all microprocessor-based systems while not causing any other damage. This would, effectively, neutralize all civil and defence systems. To guard against this kind of enemy action, electronic systems that are crucial to national defence are being provided with radiation protection.

However, the possibility of unauthorized access to national systems such as these, and of tampering with them to make them ineffective, remains. The 'Computers at Risk' report points out that we have been remarkably lucky in avoiding a disaster affecting a critical computer system, but that 'there is reason to believe our luck will soon run out'.

# Index